Date Due

1-25-66			
Fried			
OCT 2 '69			
NOV 29 '68			
Smith			
3			
	PRINTED	IN U. S. A.	

Breakthroughs

in

Science

Isaac Asimov

Breakthroughs

in

Science

Illustrated by Karoly and Szanto

Houghton Mifflin Company Boston | 1960 | *The Riverside Press Cambridge*

These essays first appeared in Senior Scholastic

Thanks are due the following individuals who acted
as consultants in the preparation of the series:

DR. JOHN R. DUNNING
Dean, School of Engineering
Columbia University, New York

DR. MAURICE EWING
Director, Lamont Geological Observatory
Palisades, New York

DR. JOHN E. NAFE
Lamont Geological Observatory
Palisades, New York

DR. ALFRED E. MIRSKY
Professor and Member
Rockefeller Institute
New York, New York

DR. HERBERT C. BROWN
Professor of Chemistry
Purdue University
Lafayette, Indiana

By the same author

Fiction

Pebble in the Sky
I, Robot
The Stars Like Dust
Foundation
Foundation and Empire
The Currents of Space
Second Foundation
The Caves of Steel
The Martian Way and Other Stories
The End of Eternity
The Naked Sun
Earth is Room Enough
The Death Dealers
Nine Tomorrows

Non-Fiction

Biochemistry and Human Metabolism*
The Chemicals of Life
Races and People*
Chemistry and Human Health*
Inside the Atom
Building Blocks of the Universe
Only a Trillion
The World of Carbon
The World of Nitrogen
Words of Science
Realm of Numbers
Realm of Measure
Breakthroughs in Science

* *in collaboration*

CONTENTS

Breakthroughs

in

Science

Archimedes

"I Can Move the World"

1

ONE MAN, it might be said, once fought an army. Ancient historians tell us that the man was old, over seventy. The army was that of the strongest power in the world — Rome itself.

But the old man, a Greek, fought the Roman army to a standstill for nearly three years — and almost won. The old man was Archimedes of Syracuse, the greatest scientist of the ancient world.

The Roman army knew his reputation well, and he lived up to it fully. Legend says that when curved mirrors were set up on the walls of Syracuse, a Greek city in Sicily, the besieging Roman ships caught fire. It wasn't sorcery; it was Archimedes. When huge claws were extended outward on beams, ships were caught, raised, and overturned. It wasn't magic; it was Archimedes.

It is said that when the besieging Romans caught a glimpse of rope or wood being raised above the walls of Syracuse, they hoisted sail and ran.

For Archimedes was different from the Greek scientists and mathematicians who had preceded him, great as

they were. Archimedes went beyond them in imagination.

For instance, to work out the areas enclosed by certain curves, he adapted existing methods of computation and came up with a system that resembled integral calculus. This was nearly two thousand years before Isaac Newton devised the modern calculus. Suppose Archimedes had had Arabic numerals to work with instead of the clumsy Greek numbers. He might have beaten Newton to the punch by 2,000 years.

Archimedes went beyond his predecessors in daring. He denied that the sands of the sea were too many to be counted. So he devised a method to count them. Not only them, but the grains of sand it would take to cover the earth. Not only that, but the grains of sand it would take to fill the universe. In doing this, he invented a new way of expressing large numbers. Our modern methods are similar in some ways to the one he devised.

Most important, Archimedes did what no man before him had done: he applied science to the problems of practical, everyday life. The great Greek mathematicians before Archimedes — Thales, Pythagoras, Eudoxus, Euclid — all considered mathematics to be abstract. It was a way of studying the majestic order of the universe — nothing more. It had no practical applications. They were intellectual snobs who despised practical applications. They considered such things fit only for merchants and slaves. Archimedes shared this snobbery to a great extent, but he was willing to apply his knowledge of mathematics to practical problems.

Archimedes was born at Syracuse, Sicily. The exact year of his birth is in doubt, but it is believed to have been 287 B.C. At that time, Sicily was a Greek land. Archimedes was the son of an astronomer and related to Hiero II, king of Syracuse from 270 to 216 B.C. He studied at Alexandria, Egypt, the intellectual center of the Mediterranean world, then returned to Syracuse and immortality.

He had been taught at Alexandria that a scientist was

above practical affairs and everyday problems. At the same time, these everyday problems fascinated Archimedes. He could not keep his mind off them. He was ashamed of this interest and refused to keep any records of his mechanical devices. But he kept on making the devices. Today his fame rests upon them.

Long before the Roman ships sailed into the harbor at Syracuse and the Roman army set up its siege, Archimedes had become renowned.

One of Archimedes' early achievements was setting up the abstract theory that explains the basic mechanics of the lever. Imagine a shaft balanced on a pivot with the length of the shaft on one side of the pivot ten times the length on the other. Pushing down the shaft at the long end moved the short end up only one-tenth the distance. However, the force pushing the long end down was multiplied ten times in the push of the short end up. In a way, distance was being exchanged for force.

Using his theory, Archimedes saw no limit to this exchange. A man had only a limited amount of force at his disposal, but distance was unlimited. Therefore, make the lever long enough, push the long end down far enough, and any weight could be lifted at the short end.

"Give me a place to stand on," he cried, "and I can move the world."

King Hiero called what he thought was a bluff. He

demanded that Archimedes move something heavy. Not
the world, perhaps, but something heavy. So Archimedes
chose a ship at the dock and had it loaded with freight
and passengers. Even empty, it could not have been
dragged out of the dock and into the sea without many
men pulling at many ropes.

But Archimedes tied the ropes together and arranged
a pulley device (a kind of lever, using ropes to take the
place of the shafts). He then pulled at the rope. Single-
handed, he drew the ship slowly into the sea.

Hiero was now quite content to believe that his great kinsman could move the earth if he wanted to. He had enough faith in him to set him seemingly impossible problems.

A goldsmith had made a gold crown for Hiero. The king wondered whether the smith had been honest. He might have kept some of the gold given him and substituted silver or copper. So Hiero ordered Archimedes to determine whether the crown was pure gold — without damaging the crown.

Archimedes was puzzled. Copper and silver were lighter than gold. If they had been added to the crown they would take up more space than would an equal weight of gold. If he knew the space taken up by the crown (that is, its volume) he could give Hiero the answer. But how was he to determine the volume of the crown without beating it into a solid mass.

Archimedes took his problem to the public baths. Probably he sighed wearily as he lowered himself into a full tub and watched the water overflow. And then he sat up, thunderstruck. For it suddenly occurred to him that his body was pushing water out of the tub. The volume of water pushed out must be equal to the volume of his body pushing in. To find the volume of anything, you merely measured the volume of the water it displaced.

He had discovered the principle of displacement in one

flash of intuition! From this he deduced the laws of buoy-
ancy and specific gravity.

Archimedes could not wait. He sprang out of the bath
and ran home through the street, naked and dripping wet.
As he ran, he cried over and over again, "I have it. I
have it." He cried it in Greek, of course, "Eureka!
Eureka!" and the word is still used today to announce a
glad discovery.

He filled a vessel with water, placed the crown in,
and measured the volume of the water displaced. Then
he did the same thing with an equal weight of pure gold.
The volume of water displaced was smaller. The gold in
the crown had been mixed with a lighter metal, giving it
greater bulk (volume), and causing more water to overflow. The king ordered the smith executed.

Even in his old age, Archimedes could not resist the
challenge of a problem. In 218 B.C., Carthage (in North
Africa) and Rome went to war with each other, and the
Carthaginian general, Hannibal, invaded Italy. He seemed
on the verge of destroying Rome. While King Hiero
lived, he kept Syracuse neutral, though in a dangerous
position between two fighting giants.

After King Hiero's death, however, a group that favored
Carthage came into power. In 213 B.C., Rome laid siege
to the city.

For three years, the aged Archimedes held off the

Roman army. But one man could do only so much. At last, in 211 B.C., the city fell. But even defeat could not affect the restless brain of Archimedes. As the soldiers swarmed into the city, he was working out a problem from a diagram. A soldier ordered him to surrender, but Archimedes paid no attention. The problem was more important to him than a little thing like the sack of a city. "Don't disturb my circles," said Archimedes.

So the soldier killed him.

The achievements of Archimedes have become part of mankind's heritage. He showed that it was possible to apply a scientific mind to the problems of everyday life. He showed that an abstract theory in pure science — the principle that explains the lever — could save the straining muscles of man.

He showed the reverse, too. By beginning with a practical problem — that of the possible adulteration of gold — he discovered a scientific principle.

Today we believe that the great duty of science is not only to *understand* the universe, but also to *better* the lot of mankind in every corner of the earth.

Johann Gutenberg

Words for the Millions

2

THE first printed edition of the world's all-time best seller was being prepared for publication in 1454. The place was Germany; the publisher was Johann Gutenberg. But rewards are unpredictable in this world. In 1455, the publisher was bankrupt for his pains.

For twenty years, Johann Gutenberg had been toiling over little oblongs of metal. All had to be exactly the same width and height, so they would fit together snugly. The top of each was molded delicately into the shape of a letter of the alphabet, carved in reverse.

Imagine those metal oblongs arranged in ranks and files tightly, with ink spread lightly and evenly over them. Imagine a sheet of paper pressed down firmly over those inked letters.

The paper is lifted. As in a conjuring trick, it is covered with ink in the shape of letters, all facing forward. The letters make up words, and the words make up the page of a book.

Men in Europe and Asia had done this before, carving words or characters in a block of wood. But such blocks

of wood were often crudely carved and good for only one "woodcut." Gutenberg's idea was to make each letter elegantly of individual metal "type." With a page completed and printed, the same type could be rearranged to produce a different page. A small collection of such movable type could be used for any book in the world. *That* was Gutenberg's vision. We might call it a triumph of technology rather than science, but it was an important breakthrough.

Scraps of Gutenberg's printed pages dating back to the 1440's exist — part of a calendar, a religious tract. In 1454, though, Gutenberg set up six presses and began to set type for the greatest of all books, the Bible.

Three hundred times a sheet of paper was pressed down on the inked type. Three hundred identical printed sheets were the result. The type was rearranged to yield another page, then another, and so on. In all, there were 1,282 different pages; 300 copies of each. Bound together, Gutenberg's pages made 300 identical copies of the Bible. This became the most important of all editions of the Bible, for it was the first printed book in the western world.

Only 45 copies of the Gutenberg Bible are in existence today. Each is priceless. To Gutenberg they brought nothing.

Gutenberg was dogged by bad luck all his life. He was born about 1398 in the city of Mainz in Germany. His parents were well-to-do. If things had gone on peacefully, Gutenberg might have been able to carry on his experiments without trouble. However, there were civil squabbles in Mainz at that time, and the Gutenberg family was on the losing side. They had to leave hurriedly for Strasbourg, 100 miles to the south. This was, perhaps, in 1430.

By 1435, Gutenberg was involved in business. Historians are not sure of the nature of the business, but he was mixed up in a lawsuit over it. In the course of the lawsuit, mention was made of "drucken," the German word for "printing."

By 1450, he was back in Mainz and definitely engaged in printing. We know because he borrowed 800 guilders from a man named Johann Fust to buy tools. All told, there must have been twenty years of experimenting, investing, laboring, and waiting — and of printing scraps of material that brought no return and created no interest.

Then, in 1454, Gutenberg began to put out his Bible, in double columns, with 42 lines in Latin to the page, and covering various pages with beautiful hand-drawn designs. Nothing was omitted in this great final gamble. It was to be the climax of Gutenberg's life. But Fust sued for his money.

Gutenberg lost the suit. He had to hand over his tools and his presses to Fust. It is probable that he didn't manage to finish the Bible. It was completed under a publishing partnership of Fust and a man named Peter Schoeffer. Fust and Schoeffer went on to become successful printers. Gutenberg sank into obscurity.

Gutenberg managed to borrow more money, to keep on printing somehow. He never gave up. But neither did he ever get out of debt. He died in Mainz about 1468, a business failure.

But printing itself was no failure. It spread with hurricane force. By 1470, there were presses in Italy, Switzerland, and France. In 1476, William Caxton established England's first printing press. In 1535, printing had crossed the Atlantic and there was a press in Mexico City.

And by that time, there was religious revolution in Europe.

In 1517, Martin Luther began his dispute with the Catholic Church, a dispute that ended in the establishment of Protestantism. There had been church reformers many times before Luther, but their influence had always been small. They could reach people only by their preaching, and the superior organization of the Church was able to stamp them out.

Luther, however, lived in a world that had the printing press. He not only preached, he wrote constantly. Dozens of his pamphlets and manifestoes were caught up by the printing press and spread thickly over Germany. In a few years, all Europe rang with the clash of different religious viewpoints.

Bibles, becoming cheaper and more plentiful, thanks to printing, were put out in the languages spoken by the people, not in Latin. Many people turned to the Bible directly for inspiration. It became possible to think of universal literacy. Before then, why teach any but a few how to read? There were so few books that reading would be a useless talent for all but a few scholars.

In short, printing created public opinion. A book like

Thomas Paine's *Common Sense* could reach every farmhouse in the American colonies and spur on our Revolutionary War as nothing else could.

Printing helped to make modern democracy possible. In ancient Greece, democracy could exist only in small cities where ideas could be spread by word of mouth. Printing, however, could multiply ideas and hurl them into every eye and mind. It could make millions of people sufficiently well informed to participate in government.

Printing could be misused, too. Wars could be made more terrible and dictatorships more powerful by the skillful use of propaganda through the printed word. The spread of literacy did not guarantee that what people read would be wise or good. Yet the benefits have been greater than the evils. Printing has made our knowledge available to future generations.

Before Gutenberg devised his little oblongs of metal, all books had been written by hand. To prepare one book took many weeks of painstaking work. To own a book was a rare thing. To own a dozen books was the mark of a rich man. To destroy just a few books might be to wipe out forever the record of a great thinker.

In the ancient world, all the vast learning and literature of Greece and Rome was compressed into a few libraries. The greatest of these, in Alexandria, Egypt, was destroyed by fire during political upheavals in the fifth century. Others disappeared as various cities fell prey to war and conquest.

Finally, only the libraries of Constantinople were left to preserve the legacy of Greece and Rome. Then, in 1204, Constantinople was sacked by Crusaders from the west. And in 1453 — the year before Gutenberg's Bible — it was captured by the Turks.

Crusaders and Turks smashed the great city, stole its treasures, destroyed most of its books and works of art. Fleeing scholars carried away what manuscripts they could, but these were pitiful remnants.

One of the greatest playwrights of all time, the Greek dramatist Sophocles, wrote about a hundred plays. We have only seven of these. We have a few scraps of Sappho's poetry, bits and pieces of various philosophers. We are fortunate to have nearly all of Homer and Herodotus, most of Plato, Aristotle, and Thucydides — but that's just luck.

A large part of ancient culture died with Constantinople.

Such a disaster could probably never happen again, thanks to printing. Any man can own hundreds of different books in inexpensive editions. Any small town can have a library that could compare in the number of its volumes to those in Alexandria and Constantinople.

Man's knowledge is as immortal as man himself now, for only the complete destruction of the human race can wipe it out.

Gutenberg may have died an apparent failure, but Gutenberg's work was one of man's great successes.

Nicolaus Copernicus

The Challenge of Infinity

3

THE old man lay on his deathbed. In 1543, Nicolaus Copernicus was seventy years old and dying. His great book was being published in a race against time. Finally, on May 24, the first printed copy of the book was laid in his nerveless hand. His glazing eyes may have seen the book, but his memory and mind were gone. He died that very day. He could not know that he had finally moved the Earth.

Seventeen hundred years earlier, Archimedes had offered to move the Earth if he were given a place to stand on. Copernicus had finally carried out that proud boast. He had found the Earth in the center of the universe, and by the power of thought he had hurled it far, far into the vastness of space. And there Earth has stayed ever since.

Copernicus was born Nicolaus Koppernigk, in Thorn (Poland), on February 19, 1473. In his lifetime, learned men wrote in Latin and adopted Latinized names, so that Koppernigk became Copernicus. The name has remained so through all the generations since.

This most notable of all Polish scientists down to the

time of Madame Curie, like other great scholars of his time, drank thirstily of knowledge all over Europe. He began by studying at the University of Cracow, where he was absorbed in mathematics and painting. In 1496, he traveled to Italy (then the very center of learning). He spent ten years there, studying medicine in Padua and law in Bologna.

He did well in every field. When he finally returned to Poland in 1506, he practiced medicine professionally, and was sought after by rich and poor. He was a member of the cathedral chapter in his diocese and administered two of the largest districts.

But it was not in law or medicine or statesmanship — though he excelled in all — that Copernicus made his mark, but in astronomy. And that, too, developed out of his Italian travels.

Italy was in an intellectual turmoil in 1500. New ideas were in the air. Old notions were being questioned. For instance, consider the theories concerning the motions of the heavenly bodies.

To begin with, all the stars, as well as the sun, the moon, and the planets circled the Earth from east to west every day. However, scholars were agreed that this was only appearance. The Earth was a globe rotating about its axis from west to east. Therefore the daily movement of the heavens was only an illusion.

If the Earth did not rotate, the stars would remain fixed in place. The moon, however, changes its position as compared with the "fixed stars." In the space of 29 days (ignoring Earth's rotation), the moon makes a complete circuit of the heavens from west to east. The sun does the same, but more slowly, taking 365 days for a circuit.

Obviously, the moon and sun rotated about the Earth. So far, so good, but it was the planets that made the trouble.

In Copernicus's time, five planets were known: Mercury, Venus, Mars, Jupiter, and Saturn. All changed their position with respect to the stars, but in an odd and complicated way. Mercury and Venus appeared sometimes in the morning, sometimes in the evening. They never appeared high in the sky, but always near the horizon (Mercury more so than Venus).

Mars, Jupiter and Saturn, on the other hand, did appear overhead on occasion. Each made a complete circle of the sky from west to east. However, their motions weren't steady. Once in each revolution, Mars slowed up, turned, and drifted for a while from east to west. This backward drift was called "retrograde motion." Jupiter went through the same backward drift twelve times in each of its longer revolutions, and Saturn thirty times in each of its still longer ones.

The ancient Greeks tried to account for this strange motion. First, they believed the universe to be governed by natural law. Therefore, they couldn't rest until they had worked out the natural law behind planetary motion. Second, they believed the motion of the planets influenced human fate. So they thought that by understanding the sky thoroughly, they could understand past and future.

About 150 A.D., the Greek mathematician and astronomer, Claudius Ptolemy, wrote a book in which he presented formulas for calculating the motions of the planets. These were based on the assumption that all the planets traveled in circular paths about the Earth.

To account for retrograde motion, he supposed that each planet traveled in a small circle and that the center of this small circle traveled west to east in a larger circle about the Earth. Occasionally, the planet would travel east to west in its smaller circle and the combination of movements would result in retrograde motion.

As observations of the heavens increased, circles had to be piled on circles. The necessary mathematics grew more and more complicated. By 1500, the Ptolemaic system had grown so top-heavy that scholars began to grow uncomfortable about it — Copernicus particularly.

Copernicus knew that a Greek mathematician, Aristarchus of Samos, had believed the Earth traveled about the sun rather than vice versa. But Aristarchus simply had

a theory and had been howled down. Copernicus believed Aristarchus was right, but he knew that he would
be howled down, too, unless he could show the theory
made sense.

Copernicus had no instruments keen enough for the
purpose. It would be three quarters of a century before
the telescope would be invented. But there still remained
the force of logic.

For one thing, if the Earth traveled about the sun,
retrograde motion was at once explained. If the Earth
were on the same side of the sun as Mars, but moved the
faster, it would gain on Mars. Mars would seem to lag
behind and move backward. Every year, Earth would
gain a lap on the outer planets — Mars, Jupiter and Saturn.
At some time each year, each of these planets would ex-
hibit retrograde motion.

If Mercury and Venus were closer to the sun than
Earth, their behavior could also be explained. Copernicus
drew diagrams to show that the inner planets would have
to follow the sun. From the Earth, they could never be
seen at more than a certain distance from the sun. Conse-
quently, Venus and Mercury could appear only in the
morning and evening, when the drowning light of the
sun was hidden by the horizon. And, of course, they
could only appear near the horizon behind which the
sun lurked.

And finally, the mathematics representing planetary motions proved to be much simpler in the Copernican system than in the Ptolemaic. What more could any one want?

But Copernicus was cautious. He knew that the most

Orbit of a planet
Orbit of the Earth

KAROLY — SZANTO.

dogmatic old diehards were often found among academic "scholars."

However, he wrote up his theory in manuscript form about 1530 and this circulated freely. He found enthusiastic followers, but also determined enemies. One was

Martin Luther, who called Copernicus a fool who denied the Bible. Copernicus felt his caution to be justified.

But in 1540, a devoted disciple of Copernicus, George Joachim Rheticus, published a summary of the Copernican theory. Pope Clement VII approved the popular summary and requested full publication of the great manuscript. Copernicus agreed. He dedicated it to the Pope, with a spirited attack on people who would use Biblical quotations to deny mathematical demonstrations.

The book, *De Revolutionibus Orbium Caelestium*, broke on Europe like a thunderbolt. But not on Copernicus. He suffered a stroke in 1542 and died on the day of publication.

He was spared the humiliation of knowing that the book had been weakened by a cowardly preface. In this preface, the truth of the Copernican theory is denied. It is presented as just a kind of trick, or mathematical hocus-pocus to simplify calculations of planetary motions.

It seems that Rheticus got into trouble (perhaps because of his Copernican views) and had to leave town. He left the publication of Copernicus's book to a friend of his, Andreas Osiander, who was a Lutheran pastor. Osiander was anxious, perhaps, to avoid seeming to deny the Bible. It was he who inserted the preface, unknown to Copernicus.

Copernicus did more than invent a theory. He changed

the relationship of man to the universe. Before his time, the Earth was all. Now Earth was only a body among other bodies in a tremendous universe.

Science stood face to face for the first time with the challenge of infinity. It met that challenge squarely, enlarging the universe constantly ever since. With one sort of infinity nobly met, another kind could be conceived, and the world of the infinitely small could be breached. Time enlarged and stretched out so that it became possible to think of Earth's history in billions of years, not thousands.

In all directions, the mind of man reached out — out — out — And he who led the way toward the infinite was Nicolaus Copernicus, who died on the very day of his great triumph.

William Harvey

Nature Was His Book

4

PATIENTLY, William Harvey had observed the action of the heart and blood. With every contraction, the heart pumped a certain quantity of blood into the arteries. At the end of one hour, it had pumped a quantity weighing three times as much as a man. Where did all that blood come from? Where did it go? Did it come from nowhere? Did it vanish into nothingness?

Harvey could see only one answer. *The blood that left the heart had to return to the heart.* The blood had to circulate about the body.

William Harvey was born on April 1, 1578, in Folkestone, England. He studied at Cambridge, then in Padua, Italy, at that time the center of medical learning. He obtained his medical degree in 1602 and became court physician to James I and later to Charles I.

His private life was uneventful. He lived at a time when England was undergoing the political upheaval of a civil war, but Harvey was never much interested in politics. His consuming interest was medical research.

Galen, the great Greek physician of the third century A.D., had thought that blood sloshed gently back and forth along the arteries, passing through invisible holes in the wall that divided the heart into two halves. First it sloshed this way, then that way. This idea held sway for 1400 years.

Many doctors of Harvey's time speculated about the movement of blood. But Harvey sought within the body itself for clues that would explain the mystery. Here he followed in the footsteps of Andreas Vesalius, a great Belgian physician who had taught at Padua only a generation before Harvey had studied there. Vesalius, the first to dissect human bodies, was the father of the science of anatomy.

Harvey studied the beating hearts of living animals and noted that the two halves did not contract simultaneously. He studied the valves between the ventricles and the auricles, those small chambers of the heart, and noted they were one-way valves. He studied the valves in veins, which also were one-way. These had been discovered by Harvey's teacher in Padua, a physician named Fabricius, but he did not understand their function.

Obviously, blood could flow away from the heart in arteries and toward the heart in veins. The valves prevented any flow in reverse.

He tied off arteries and noticed that they bulged with pressure only on the side toward the heart. He did the same with veins. The pressure was on the side away from the heart. By 1616, he was certain the blood circulated.

There was only one flaw in the theory. There were no visible connections between arteries and veins. How did the blood pass from one to the other? The arterial system was like a tree in which the branches divide into

smaller and smaller twigs. Near the point where the arteries seemed to come to an end, tiny veins arose. They grew larger and larger, but there was no actual connection between them and the arteries.

By 1628, however, Harvey was convinced of his theory despite the flaw. He published a 52-page book with a long Latin title. It is commonly known as *De Motus Cordis* ("Concerning the Motion of the Heart"). It was printed on thin, cheap paper and was full of typographical errors, but it overthrew Galen's theory.

At first, the results were not so desirable, from Harvey's standpoint. His practice fell off. He was jeered by his opponents, and patients did not wish to trust themselves to a crackpot. He was called "Circulator," not because he believed in the circulation of the blood, but because that was Latin slang for "quack," the name given to peddlers who hawked medicines at the circus.

Through it all, Harvey maintained silence and kept on with his work. He knew he would be proved right.

He was. The final proof came in 1661, four years after Harvey's death. An Italian doctor, Marcello Malpighi, examined living tissue through a microscope. He found tiny blood vessels connecting the arteries and veins in the lungs of a frog. He called them capillaries ("hairlike") because of their smallness. The theory of circulation was complete.

The importance of Harvey's work lies in the methods he used. He substituted observation for "authority" and looked at nature instead of at dusty ancient manuscripts. From that beginning grew the monumental life-sciences of today.

Galileo Galilei

"But It Does Move"

5

SLOWLY, the old man got down on his knees before the judges of the Inquisition. With his head bent, his tired voice said what had to be said. He denied the sun was the center of the universe, and admitted he had been wrong to teach that it was. He denied that the Earth turned on its axis or revolved about the sun, and admitted he had been wrong to teach that it did.

On that day, June 22, 1633, the Churchmen sitting as a tribunal for the Inquisition at Rome felt they had won a victory. Galileo Galilei, at 69, was the most renowned scientist in Europe. He was also famous for his writings, which gave his views so clearly, and so effectively ridiculed his opponents.

Now he had been forced to admit he was wrong. The Inquisition, mindful of his fame, had treated him gently and now allowed him to return to Florence. There he spent the last eight years of his life, working on non-controversial problems. He never disturbed the Church with heretical opinions again. On January 8, 1642, he died.

Galileo (he is universally known by his first name only) was born in Pisa on February 15, 1564. From the very beginning, he showed the wide range of his creative interests. As a boy, he showed unusual skill in designing toys. As he grew up, he played the organ and the lute, wrote songs, poems, and literary criticism. He even attracted attention as a painter. He was vaguely unhappy with his first years of schooling at a monastery in Florence. His father wanted him to be a physician, but Galileo was even less happy when he went to the University of Pisa in 1581 to study medicine.

In Pisa his mind began moving in other directions. Attending services at the Cathedral of Pisa, he found himself watching a chandelier swinging in the air currents. Sometimes it swung in a wide arc. Sometimes it swung in a narrow arc. There was nothing unusual about this, but 17-year-old Galileo noticed something others had not seen.

He felt for his pulse and began counting. So many pulse beats for a wide quick swing; so many for a narrower slow swing. But always the same number of pulse beats whether the swing was wide or narrow. Galileo had discovered the law of the pendulum.

But if a pendulum swung constantly, biting off equal little fragments of time, so to speak, this offered a new and revolutionary method for measuring time. Galileo had used his pulse to time a pendulum. But the pendulum could also be used to time the human pulse. Galileo passed on this information to his professors.

Galileo never got his degree in medicine. He did not have enough money to continue his studies. The real reason, however, was probably lack of interest. By chance, he overheard a lecture on geometry, and discovered he was really interested in mathematics and physics — not medicine.

He went to Florence, found a patron, and studied the behavior of objects floating in water. His essay describing his conclusions was so well done that it made him an obvious "young hopeful" in the scholarly world of Italy. When he returned to Pisa in 1588, it was as a mathematical lecturer at the University. There, he proceeded to study falling bodies.

Aristotle had believed (2,000 years before) that the speed with which a body fell was in ratio to its weight. Scholars ever since had agreed. After all, do not feathers fall very slowly? Why argue with the evidence of your eyes?

Galileo thought that air resistance might be playing a part, slowing up light objects that had a large surface area. To demonstrate this (the story goes), he climbed to the top of the Leaning Tower of Pisa with two cannon balls of equal size, one of cast iron and one of wood. The cast iron ball was ten times heavier than the wood ball. If Aristotle (and the professors at Pisa) were right, the iron ball should fall ten times faster than the wooden ball. Would it? A large crowd (says the story) was watching to see the answer.

Galileo dropped them carefully over the railing simultaneously. Thwack! They hit the ground with a single clap of sound.

Aristotle could not have been proved more thoroughly wrong. At 27, Galileo had destroyed authority (and also the dignity of his fellow professors). He had to leave Pisa, but he had a better job waiting for him at the University of Padua. And there the real glory of his life was to come.

Rumors from Holland told of a tube with lenses that made far objects appear near at hand. The Dutch government had clamped the lid of military secrecy on the invention, but Galileo got to thinking about how such a device might work.

In six months, he had designed and constructed a telescope (later he constructed many others which were distributed over Europe). He demonstrated it in Venice, where it was a sensation. Portly gentlemen puffed up stairs to the tops of the highest buildings to look through Galileo's tube at ships so distant they would not arrive in the harbor for hours.

But Galileo thought neither of war nor of commerce. He pointed his telescope at the sky. There he found mountains and craters on the moon; new stars, invisible to the naked eye, in Orion. He found Venus showed phases like our moon and the sun had spots.

It was on January 7, 1610, that he made the crucial discovery. He looked at Jupiter and at once found four little "stars" near it. He followed them night after night. There could be no mistake. They were four moons circling Jupiter, each in its own orbit. They were the final disproof of the old notion that everything in the heavens rotated about the Earth. Here certainly were four objects that were rotating about Jupiter.

Galileo brought his telescope to Rome in 1611. Many at the Papal court were impressed, but some were angered. Was this man, who had already destroyed Aristotle's notions about falling bodies, now to destroy Aristotle's doctrines that the heavens were perfect? How could there be rough mountains on the heavenly face of the moon and spots on the perfect sun?

"See for yourself," said Galileo. "Look through my instrument."

Many refused. Some said that the moons of Jupiter could not be seen by the naked eye, were therefore of no use to humanity, and could not have been created. If the instrument showed them, the instrument was wrong.

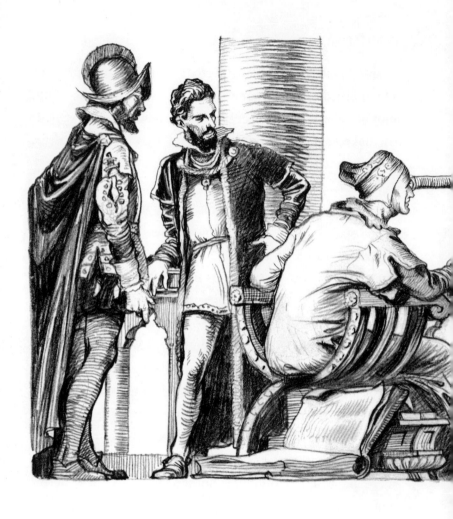

It was flawed, said some, a device of the devil. Galileo
was supported by one faction of the Church, and attacked
by another.

    Galileo wrote articles about his discoveries. In them,
he defended himself against his attackers with sarcastic

anger. He began to take up a bolder and bolder position
in favor of the theories of Copernicus.

Galileo had a knack for making his opponents look
ridiculous, and they rarely forgave him for it. This time
his opponents were powerful men in the Church. As a

result of pressure from these men, the Church finally declared, in 1616, that belief in the Copernican system was a heresy. Pope Pius V then instructed Galileo to abandon Copernicanism.

For fifteen years, Galileo did — at least in public. He kept quiet, worked on other things, and waited for the Church to ease its position. For some reason, he seemed to think the Church had. Without apparently anticipating trouble, in 1632 he published his great defense of the Copernican system. In it, he poked merciless fun at his opponents. And the Inquisition called him to Rome.

Then followed the long and wearying trial of the aged scientist. There is a story that when Galileo rose from his knees, after swearing the Earth stood still, he said something softly under his breath. What did he mutter? The story goes that he said: "But it does move."

Why do we honor Galileo today? His discoveries and inventions staggered the imagination of Europe at his time. He was a versatile and original scientist. In addition to those "firsts" we have already discussed, Galileo scored a number of other achievements. He found a way to measure the weight of bodies in water. He devised a thermometer to measure temperature. He built a water clock to measure time. He proved air has weight, was the first to use the telescope in astronomy.

Yet it is not for these alone that Galileo holds so lofty

a place in the hierarchy of science. Why, then, do we honor him?

First, Galileo discovered the laws that govern force and motion and the speed of moving objects. And then he stated these laws of dynamics in mathematical formulas, rather than in words. Yet Galileo was no amateur with words. He was the first scientist to abandon Latin and write in his native tongue. And his style and wit brought his work to the attention of all Europe. Even princes traveled to Italy to sit in his classes.

Second, Galileo demolished the pedantic approach to science. It was not only that he observed things for him-

self and based his deductions on actual experiments and tests. That had been done before Galileo by other scientists who sought truth in nature, not in dusty old manuscripts.

Galileo was the first to arrive at his conclusions by the modern scientific method of combining observation with logic. And he expressed his logic in mathematics — the clear, unmistakable picture language of science.

Anton Van Leeuwenhoek

He Discovered an Invisible World

6

ANTON VAN LEEUWENHOEK was a draper with only a few years schooling. But he discovered a new world more amazing than the one discovered by Columbus. His hobby was making little glass lenses. One day he studied a drop of stagnant water through one of his lenses. There he saw what no one before him had ever seen or imagined. Tiny animals, too small to be seen by the naked eye, were moving and feeding and being born and dying in a drop of water that was a whole universe to them.

Van Leeuwenhoek was born in the city of Delft, Holland, on October 24, 1632. He lived in Delft all his 90 years. He left school at 16, when his father died, and became a clerk in a dry-goods store. Later he was appointed janitor at the Delft City Hall. He held this position for the rest of his life.

But he had his hobby, grinding tiny, perfect lenses. Some of these were only one eighth of an inch across. But they magnified objects 200 times without distortion.

Of course, everyone knew that lenses made objects appear larger. But most scientists had only mediocre lenses.

Van Leeuwenhoek ground excellent lenses. He mounted the lenses in oblongs of copper, silver, or gold. He would fix an object on one side of the lens. Then he would stare at it for hours. Often, he left the object there for months or even permanently. If he wanted to look at another object, he ground another lens. In his lifetime he ground a total of 419 lenses.

He looked at everything: insects, drops of water, toothscrapings, bits of meat, hair, seeds. Whatever he saw, he drew and described with painstaking accuracy.

In 1665, van Leeuwenhoek looked at living capillaries. These tiny vessels connecting arteries and veins had been discovered four years earlier by an Italian. But van Leeuwenhoek was the first to see blood moving through them. And in 1674, he discovered the red corpuscles that give blood its color.

In 1683, he made perhaps his most important discovery:

bacteria. They were too tiny for his lenses to magnify clearly, nor did he know the significance of his discovery.

These discoveries were not kept secret. In 1660, a number of Englishmen interested in science had been encouraged by King Charles II to form an official society. It has a long name but is usually called simply the Royal Society.

Van Leeuwenhoek wrote long letters to the Royal Society, describing in detail his lenses and all he saw through them. The society was astonished, and probably unwilling to believe him at first. In 1677, however, Robert Hooke of the society built microscopes according to van Leeuwenhoek's instructions. He found exactly what van Leeuwenhoek said he would find. There was no question after that, particularly after van Leeuwenhoek sent 26 of his microscopes as a gift to the society, so that the members could all see for themselves.

In 1680, van Leeuwenhoek was elected a Fellow of the Royal Society. A poorly schooled draper was its most famous foreign member. In his long lifetime, van Leeuwenhoek sent a total of 375 scientific papers to the Royal Society and 27 papers to the French Academy of Science. Though he never left Delft, his work made him world famous.

The Dutch East India Company sent him insects from Asia to put under his marvelous lenses. The Queen of

England paid him a visit. When Peter the Great, Czar of Russia, visited Holland to learn ship-building, he took time out to pay his respects to van Leeuwenhoek.

Did van Leeuwenhoek let the queen or the czar look through his lenses? He did, though he disliked having anyone finger his beloved microscopes.

Van Leeuwenhoek was not the first to construct a microscope, nor the first to use one. However, he was the first to demonstrate what could be done with one. He was the first to use one so well that single-handedly he established the basis for most of modern biology.

Without the ability to see cells and to study them, the modern anatomist and physiologist would be helpless. Without the ability to see bacteria and to study them and their life cycles, modern medicine probably would still be in the dark ages.

All the discoveries of the great biologists since 1700 stem, in one way or another, from the tiny glass lenses painstakingly ground by the janitor of Delft City Hall.

Isaac Newton

"All Was Light"

7

In 1666, so the story goes, when Isaac Newton was 23 years old, he saw an apple fall from a tree. He had seen this happen before. So had countless others. But this time Newton looked upward. A pale half-moon was visible in the daytime sky over the English countryside. Newton asked himself: Why does not the moon, too, fall to the Earth, as the apple fell, drawn by the force of gravity?

Newton reasoned as follows: Perhaps the moon *is* pulled to the Earth, but the speed of the moon's movement through space cancels out the pull of the Earth's gravity. He reasoned further: If the force that pulls the apple to the Earth also pulls the moon to the Earth, that force would have to extend far out into space. And as it extended into space, this force of gravity would become weaker and weaker.

Newton calculated the distance of the moon from the Earth's center. Then he calculated how fast the moon would have to travel in its orbit to balance the pull of Earth's gravity at that distance from the Earth. The answer he found checked pretty nearly with the figures given by astronomers for the speed of the moon. But it did not check *exactly*. The theory must be wrong, thought Newton. He put it aside.

Newton was already making his mark in mathematics, though as a youngster he had shown little promise. He was born on Christmas Day of 1642 (the year Galileo died) in Woolsthorpe, England. His father, a farmer, had died the day before young Isaac was born. As a boy, Newton was a dull student until (the story goes) he grew tired of being beaten up by the bright boy of the class. Newton applied himself until *he* was first in the class.

By the time he was 18, Newton's interest in mathematics was arousing attention. He would make a poor farmer, said his uncle, and he talked Newton's mother into sending the young man to Cambridge University. Nine years later, Newton was professor of mathematics at Cambridge.

But what years these were for Newton! He studied beams of light, for instance. He allowed sunlight to enter a darkened room through a hole in a curtain. The tiny beam of light then was passed through a triangular glass prism. The light fell on a screen as a rainbow band —

A. KAROLY· L·SZANTO·

not as a spot of white light. Newton was the first to discover that white light was actually made up of various colors which could be separated and recombined.

At the same time, he blazed new frontiers in mathematics. He worked out the binomial theorem for expressing certain algebraic quantities. Much more important, he discovered a new way for calculating areas bounded by curves. (At almost the same time, the German mathematician Wilhelm Leibniz discovered this independently.) Newton called his new technique "fluxions." We call it "calculus."

Even Newton's mistakes were fruitful in their results. Newton had developed a theory to explain his discovery that white light could be bent by glass into a rainbow. The theory was wrong, as scientists found later. But it seemed to explain why the early telescopes, which were constructed of lenses that bent or "refracted" light, formed images surrounded by small colored blurs. This was called "chromatic aberration." Newton's wrong theory led him to believe that this chromatic aberration could never be corrected.

For this reason, he decided to make telescopes without lenses. He designed telescopes that used parabolic mirrors to gather and concentrate light by reflection. He built his first in 1668. These "reflecting telescopes" had no chromatic aberration.

Shortly after Newton died, telescopes were built using special lenses that did *not* show chromatic aberration. However, the best and largest telescopes still use the reflecting principle. The 200-inch telescope atop Mt. Palomar in California is a reflecting telescope.

But Newton's attempt to apply Earth's gravity to the moon remained a failure. The years passed, and it seemed dead for good.

As it happened, one of Newton's faults was that he couldn't take criticism, and he kept up feuds. Newton and his followers, for instance, fought a battle with Leibniz and his followers over who first invented calculus, when both deserved credit.

In the Royal Society of London (of which Newton was a member), Newton's great enemy was Robert Hooke. Hooke was a capable scientist, but he had a grass-hopper mind. He started things and dropped them. He started so many things that no matter what anyone else did, Hooke could always claim he had thought of it first.

In 1684, Hooke — in the company of Edmund Halley, a very good friend of Newton's — boasted that he had worked out the laws explaining the force that controlled the motions of the heavenly bodies. His theory didn't seem satisfactory, and arguments began.

Halley went to Newton and asked him how the planets would move if there were a force of attraction between bodies that weakened as the square of the distance.

Newton said at once, "In ellipses."

"But how do you know?"

"Why, I have calculated it." And Newton told his friend the story of his attempt 18 years earlier, and how it had failed. Halley, in a frenzy of excitement, urged Newton to try again.

Now things were different. In 1666, Newton had *supposed* that the force of attraction acted from Earth's center, but he hadn't been able to prove it. Now he had calculus as a tool. With his new mathematical techniques, he could *prove* that the force acted from the center. Also, during the last 18 years, new and better measurements had been made of the radius of the Earth, and of the moon's size and its distance from the Earth.

This time, Newton's theory checked the facts — exactly. The moon was pulled to the Earth, held in Earth's grip by gravity, just as the apple.

In 1687, Newton expounded his theory in a book, *Philosophiae Naturalis Principia Mathematica*. In it, he also announced the "Three Laws of Motion." The third of these states that for every action there is an equal and opposite reaction. It is this principle which explains how rocket engines work.

The Royal Society intended to publish the book, but there was not enough money in the treasury. Also, Hooke was raising all the trouble he could, insisting he had the idea first. Halley, who was well-to-do, therefore published the book at his own expense.

But the great days of Newton were over. In 1692, that all-embracing mind tottered. Newton had a nervous breakdown and had to spend nearly two years in retirement. To burn up his boundless mental energies, he turned toward theology and alchemy, as though science were not enough. He wasted his powers on a search for ways to manufacture gold.

He was never the same after his nervous breakdown, though at times he showed flashes of his old genius. In 1696, for example, a Swiss mathematician challenged Europe's scholars to solve two problems. The day after Newton saw the problems he forwarded the solutions anonymously. The Swiss mathematician penetrated the disguise at once. "I recognize the claw of the lion," he said.

Newton was appointed Warden of the Mint in 1696, and placed in charge of coinage. He resigned his professorship to attend to his new duties. These he did so well that he was a virtual terror to counterfeiters.

He even served in Parliament for two terms, elected as a representative of Cambridge University. He never made a speech. On one occasion he rose, and the House fell silent to hear the great man. All Newton did was ask that the window be closed because there was a draft.

In 1705, Newton was knighted by Queen Anne. On March 20, 1727, forty years after his great discoveries, Newton died.

Newton is important for more than his great discoveries. To be sure, his laws of motion completed the work begun by Galileo. And his laws of universal gravity explained the work of Copernicus and Kepler, as well as the movement of the tides. These great concepts live today in every branch of mechanics. He founded the science of optics, which enabled us to learn as much as we have about the composition of the stars and almost all we have learned about the composition of matter. The value of calculus in every branch of science is beyond estimate.

Yet Newton's greatest importance to the advance of science may be psychological. The reputation of the ancient Greek philosophers and scholars had been badly shaken by the discoveries of such moderns as Galileo and Harvey. But Europe's scientists still suffered a sense of inferiority.

Then came Newton. His gravitational theories opened a vision of the universe greater and grander than anything Aristotle had dreamed of. His elegant system of celestial mechanics brought the heavens within the reach of man's intelligence, showing that the most remote heavenly bodies were subject to precisely the same laws as the smallest mundane object.

His theories became models of what a scientific theory should be. In all other sciences, and in political and moral philosophy also, writers and thinkers since Newton have attempted to emulate his elegant simplicity. They used rigorous formulae and a few basic principles.

Here was a mind as great as any of the ancients. His contemporaries knew it. Newton was almost idolized in his own lifetime. When he died, he was buried in Westminster Abbey with England's heroes. Voltaire of France, who was visiting England at the time, commented with admiration that England honored a mathematician as other nations honor a king.

From Newton's day, science has been filled with a self-confidence that never again faltered.

Newton's glory is perhaps best expressed in a couplet by Alexander Pope.

Nature and Nature's laws lay hid in night.
God said, Let Newton be! and all was light.

James Watt

He Started Two Revolutions

8

JAMES WATT studied the steam engine before him carefully. It was a model of an engine first built by Thomas Newcomen about 1705, sixty years before. The engine was used to pump water out of mines. The model belonged to the University of Glasgow in Scotland, where Watt worked as a mathematical-instrument maker.

"This isn't working well," the professor said. "Fix it!"

In the engine, steam from boiling water was allowed to enter a chamber topped by a movable piston. The steam pressure pushed the piston upward. Then cold water was run into the chamber to cool it. The steam condensed and the piston sank. More steam; up went the piston. More cold water; down went the piston. The up and down motion of the piston worked the pump.

The process took immense quantities of steam, thought Watt, and yet the engine worked so inefficiently. There was more power to steam than that.

Watt, a trained engineer with an analytical mind, began to study steam scientifically. To exert maximum power, steam must first be as hot as possible. Then it must be converted to water as cold as possible. But wasn't that what Newcomen's engine did?

One Sunday, early in the year 1765, Watt took a solitary walk, thinking. He came to a sudden halt. Why, of course! Steam was being wasted because at each step the chamber was being cooled down. The next gush of steam had to heat up the chamber before it could move the piston.

Watt rushed back to his workshop and began putting together a new kind of steam engine. After the steam entered the chamber and moved the piston, it escaped through a valve into a *second* chamber cooled by running water. As the steam escaped, the piston sank. A new rush of steam into the first chamber wasted none of its power since that chamber was *still hot*.

Watt had a steam engine that worked efficiently. His achievement was a triumph of technology, not of science. But that Sunday walk helped to change the future of the world.

The new steam engine replaced the old Newcomen

machine almost at once in the mines. Watt kept making improvement after improvement. For instance, he let steam enter the chamber at each end, thus pushing the piston both ways alternately. This increased the efficiency still more.

Watt's invention meant power! Before Watt, there had been the muscles of man and of animals. There had been wind and falling water. But Watt made possible the first practical use of a power greater than any of them. (The unit of power called the "watt" is named in his honor.) Many of these uses he conceived himself.

Steam engines could be used to drive heavy machinery. For the first time, large amounts of power could be concentrated in a small area. Factories and mass production became possible.

Furthermore, England was then short of charcoal for fuel. She had exhausted her forests. The timber that was left had to be reserved for the Navy. The alternative was coal. But coal mines were difficult to work because of water seepage. The Watt steam engine pumped out the water efficiently and a flood of cheap coal became available. Burning coal produced steam. Steam produced power. The Industrial Revolution had begun!

Today, we are in a second Industrial Revolution. This one, too, dates back to an invention by James Watt.

To keep the flow of steam into his engines constant,

Watt made the steam whirl two weights held by hinged rods to a vertical shaft. Gravity pulled those weights down, centrifugal force (as the weights whirled about) kept them up. If too much steam entered the chamber, the rotation of the weights became faster. They were forced up. This motion partially closed a valve, choking off the steam. As the steam pressure fell, the weights rotated more slowly, dropped, and opened the valve. More steam could enter.

Thus, the amount of steam was kept within narrow limits. The steam engine was equipped with a "brain" that could correct its failures automatically and continuously. This is what is meant by "automation." Today, the science of automation has reached the point where whole factories can be made to run without man's interference, correcting their own errors by devices using the basic principle of James Watt's "centrifugal governor."

Watt was also an able and respected civil engineer who had much to do with the planning of bridges, canals and harbor facilities. He died on August 19, 1819, after a ripe and peaceful old age. He lived to see the Industrial Revolution well begun. But he never dreamed that he also had started a second Industrial Revolution that would not come into its own for nearly two centuries.

Antoine-Laurent Lavoisier

Father of Modern Chemistry

9

FRANCE was in turmoil. The Revolution, which had begun in 1789 with the storming of the Bastille, was growing more violent. By 1792, the "Reign of Terror" had begun. The extremists were bent on revenge against those who had participated in injustices during the days of the kings.

For instance there was the *Ferme générale*, a private organization that had collected taxes on salt, tobacco, and other items for the government. The organization paid the government a fixed sum. Anything collected over that sum was kept. Most of the collectors gouged every cent they could. Naturally, the peasants, laborers and middle classes hated them.

In November 1792, the order went out to arrest all former members of the organization. One of these was Antoine-Laurent Lavoisier, a renowned chemist. He had not only been a member, he had even married the daughter of the head of the firm.

When they came to arrest him, he protested that he was involved in no politics, that the money he had made as a tax-collector had gone to pay for scientific experiments. "I am a scientist," he exclaimed.

The arresting officer said roughly, "The Republic has no need of scientists." (He was wrong, of course. The Republic *did* need them and encouraged them, except when mob passions were aroused.)

On May 2, 1794, France's foremost scientist lost his head under the guillotine. It was probably the greatest single loss of the Revolution. The execution of a mere king was as nothing in comparison.

Count Lagrange, the great French astronomer, mourned afterward: "A moment was all that was necessary to strike off his head, and probably a hundred years will not be sufficient to produce another like it."

Ten weeks after the execution, the extremists were themselves executed and the Reign of Terror was over. It was ten weeks too late.

Lavoisier, until that sad end, lived a successful life. He was born in Paris, on August 26, 1743. His father was a well-to-do lawyer. Young Lavoisier had no trouble obtaining an excellent education. He took a degree in law, but studied various sciences and decided he liked science better.

He joined the *Ferme générale* and used the funds he earned, plus money he inherited from his mother, to equip an excellent laboratory for his own use. He married in 1771. His wife, a skilled artist, prepared drawings for his books, and helped take notes on his experiments.

From the beginning, Lavoisier realized the importance of accuracy. His experiments were characterized by careful weighings, meticulous measurement, and detailed notes. They made enough of an impression to admit him to the *Académie Royale des Sciences* in 1768, when he was 25.

It was in the next year, though, that he first showed the importance of accuracy. There were still chemists who believed in the old doctrine of "four elements": fire, air, water, and earth. They thought that if water were heated long enough, it would turn to earth. As proof

they pointed to the sediment that appeared in water that had been boiling for a long time.

Lavoisier was not content merely to look. He heated water for 101 days. Sure enough, a sediment appeared. But he weighed the glass vessel which held the water, both before and after the heating. The weight lost by the glass, he showed, was just equal to the weight of the sediment. The sediment came from changes in the glass, not from the water.

Lavoisier was a public-spirited man. He joined any number of commissions and boards that investigated the miserable conditions of the peasants. This connection with the government worked against him at his trial. Even

so — though the Revolutionary judges blinded themselves to it — one of Lavoisier's government services had important consequences for all humanity.

He had been asked to make a study of practical methods for lighting cities at night. In making this study, he had to consider various fuels for burning in lamps. This got him interested in the general problem of burning or combustion.

At that time, combustion was explained by means of the "phlogiston theory," which had been first announced about 70 years earlier. The theory held that metals were composed of a "calx" (what we would call a "rust" or an "oxide") plus a mysterious substance called phlogiston. When a metal was heated, the phlogiston escaped, leaving the calx behind.

The theory was all wrong, of course, and it led chemists into even worse confusion. For instance, it was shown that the calx weighed more than the original metal. The only way to explain that was to suppose that phlogiston had negative weight!

In 1772, Lavoisier opened his attack on the problem. He and other chemists pooled money to buy a diamond. Heat was concentrated upon it by means of a large magnifying lens, and the diamond burnt away completely. Lavoisier also burned sulfur and phosphorus, and heated tin and lead to form a calx. He concluded that burning and calx-formation involved the same natural process.

Sulfur, phosphorus, tin, and lead all gained weight when heated to burning or to calx. Some scientists had suggested that the weight increased because the materials gained "fire particles." Was it loss of phlogiston or gain of fire?

Lavoisier settled the matter neatly. He heated tin in a closed vessel. Part of it changed to a calx, but there was no gain at all in weight! After he opened the vessel, however, air rushed in. *Then* there was a gain in weight. Apparently, the metal, when heated, absorbed something out of the air, forming a heavier calx and a partial vacuum. The weight gained by the calx was lost by the air.

Lavoisier's experiments led him to believe that in any chemical reaction in a closed system there was neither gain nor loss of weight. His careful measurements told him that. This was the first statement of the important Law of Conservation of Mass. This means that matter can neither be created nor destroyed. Through chemical action it can only be changed from one form into another. From this point it was only a step to the working out of chemical equations. These show that the mass of materials before any chemical change must equal the mass of the products created by the change.

In 1774, Joseph Priestley, the British clergyman who had discovered oxygen, visited Paris and talked with

Lavoisier. Lavoisier saw the importance of oxygen at once. Back to his experiments! He showed that when charcoal burnt in air, or metal formed a calx, only part of the air was consumed, and the air left over would not support combustion. If, however, pure oxygen were used, substances burnt or formed calxes much more easily and quickly than in ordinary air, and all the oxygen was used up.

Lavoisier recognized that both oxygen and nitrogen

(he called the latter *azote*, meaning "no life") were present in air, and that combustion (and life, too) depended upon combination with oxygen.

By 1786, Lavoisier published a paper he had prepared three years earlier, which summarized his experiments. He gave the interpretation of combustion which we still use today. Phlogiston was killed dead as a doornail once and for all.

In 1787, Lavoisier, together with three other chemists, published a book called *Méthode de nomenclature chimique*, in which were laid down logical rules for naming chemical compounds. Until then, names had been made up at the whim of the individual chemist. Today, when we speak of sodium chloride or of potassium chlorate, we are using names that fit Lavoisier's scheme.

Finally, in 1789, Lavoisier crowned his work by publishing a textbook of chemistry called *Traité élémentaire de chimie*. In it he incorporated the new notions he had developed. It was the first modern chemistry textbook.

At the very climax of his work, in the same year his textbook was published, the French Revolution broke out. In early 1792 he was forced out of his laboratory. A few months later he was arrested. His useful life ended in tragedy for himself and the world when he was only 51.

Lavoisier is called the "Father of Modern Chemistry." The name is a deserved one. With boundless energy and insight, he lifted chemistry out of a dead-end and put it on the right road.

Undoubtedly, if he had not lived, some other chemist or a group of chemists might have come to Lavoisier's conclusions. But it is difficult to see how one individual could have done more in a shorter time than did Lavoisier.

His idea that chemists must measure and weigh accurately was perhaps his most important single contribution. Chemists have never forgotten the lesson, and have labored to be "quantitative" ever since. The miracles of chemistry today — new alloys, fuels, explosives, fibers, plastics and so on — all date back to the man who gave chemistry its new outlook and taught chemists the proper way to experiment.

Michael Faraday

Magnetism Becomes Electricity

1 0

AN ENGLISH physicist was lecturing before an audience in London about 120 years ago on some of the tricks that could be performed with magnets and wires. He had a coil of wire hooked up to a galvanometer. This is an instrument used to measure electricity. It has a needle which moves when current flows through the instrument. Of course, since the galvanometer was not connected to any battery, there could be no current flowing through it. The needle was motionless.

But watch! The lecturer lowered a bar magnet into the coil. The needle jerked to the right. From nowhere, apparently, an electric current had appeared. He removed the magnet. The needle kicked again, this time to the left. Very curious!

After the lecture, one story goes, an earnest woman out of the audience approached the lecturer. "But, Mr. Faraday, of what use is the electricity set up for just a split-second by that magnet?"

Very politely, Michael Faraday asked in return, "Madam, of what use is a new-born baby?"

Another version of the story is that a politician asked him the question and that Faraday had retorted, "Sir, in twenty years you will be taxing that electricity."

Michael Faraday was born near London on September 22, 1791. His father, a hard-working blacksmith with ten children, moved his family to London when Faraday was a lad.

There, young Faraday was apprenticed to a bookbinder. This was a stroke of luck, for it exposed him to books. Officially, he was concerned only with the outside of books, but he could not help opening the pages and dipping into the inside as well. Nor could he help becoming interested in science.

Faraday had a second stroke of luck. His employer encouraged young Faraday to read the books and allowed him to attend scientific lectures as well.

Faraday attended the lectures with great enthusiasm. He took extensive notes, and when he came home he would write them up carefully, adding his own diagrams to make them clearer. The lectures he enjoyed most were those given by Humphrey Davy of the Royal Institution. Davy was England's most famous chemist and a very popular lecturer. Faraday sent him a copy of the notes he had taken of the lectures, and asked for a job as Davy's laboratory assistant.

Davy read the notes with pleasure and amazement. At

the first opportunity he gave Faraday the job he requested. Faraday was 22 when he took the job at the Royal Institution, at a salary that was smaller than the one he had been earning as a bookbinder.

Davy had invented the miners' safety lamp and the carbon arc. He had discovered numerous chemical substances, including eight new elements. Yet it is usually said that his greatest discovery was Michael Faraday.

Faraday virtually lived in the laboratory and showed himself worthy of his master in every respect. After Davy died in 1829, Faraday took his place. In 1833, he was appointed professor of chemistry.

Faraday carried on Davy's most famous work. Davy had isolated most of the elements he had discovered by separating them out of chemical compounds by means of an electric current. Faraday discovered that the electricity required to liberate the unit equivalent mass of any element is precisely the same. That is, the same electricity liberates the same number of atoms. Faraday's researches led to the modern concept of the electron.

But Faraday was fascinated by magnets. He sprinkled iron filings on paper held over the poles of magnets and noticed how the filings lined up between the poles in definite patterns. Magnets, he said, were surrounded by invisible "fields of force." The filings made "lines of force" visible.

Thus, it was only natural for Faraday to become interested in the connection between electricity and magnetism. In 1820, a Danish scientist, Hans Christian Oersted, had found that wires through which electricity was flowing showed magnetic properties.

If electricity set up a magnetic field, thought Faraday, why should not a magnetic field set up electricity? He worked out an experiment to test this. He wound a coil of wire around one segment of an iron ring. This coil was attached to a battery. The circuit could be opened and closed by a key. If he closed the circuit a magnetic field would be set up in the coil, as Oersted had shown, and it would be carried through the iron.

Then a second coil was wrapped around another segment of the iron ring. This coil was connected directly to a galvanometer. If Faraday's theory was right, the magnetic field created in the iron ring by the first coil would set up a current in the second coil. This current would be indicated by the galvanometer.

On August 29, 1831, Faraday tried the experiment. It didn't work! At least, not as he thought it would. The magnetic field itself created no current. *But starting or breaking the field set up a current.* When Faraday closed the circuit in the first coil, the galvanometer attached to the second coil kicked its needle. When he broke the circuit, the needle kicked again, in the opposite direction.

Faraday decided that it was not the magnetic lines of force in themselves that set up the current. It was the *motion* of these lines across a wire. When the current started in the first coil of wire, the magnetic field sprang into being. Expanding lines of force cut across the wire of the second coil. When the current was broken, the magnetic field died. The collapsing lines of force again cut across the wire of the second coil.

He showed this fact more plainly to himself and to audiences by inserting a magnet into a coil of wire. Only while the magnet was being placed in the coil or taken out did current flow in the coil. It would also flow if the magnet were motionless and the coil were being placed over it or removed. But if both magnet and coil were motionless, there was no current.

Faraday had discovered how to make magnetism induce

an electric current to flow. He had discovered "electro-magnetic induction."

Two months later, Faraday took the next step. How could he produce a continuous current out of magnetism in some convenient way? He set up a thin copper wheel which could be turned on a shaft. Its outer rim passed between the poles of a strong magnet as it turned.

As it turned between the poles, the wheel cut lines of magnetic force constantly, so that a current of electricity was constantly flowing through the wheel. Two wires, ending in two sliding contacts, were attached to this gadget. One contact brushed against the copper wheel as it turned. The other brushed against the shaft. A galvanometer in the circuit showed that as long as the copper wheel turned, a continuous current was generated.

In this way, Faraday generated electricity out of mechanical motion. He had invented the first electric "generator."

Electrical induction can play interesting tricks. Electrical power is determined by two things: the quantity of electricity passing through a conductor per second (amperage), and the force driving the electricity (voltage). When a current in one coil induces a current in a second coil, the power in both coils must be the same, but the details can vary. For instance, if the second coil has twice as many loops of wire as the first coil does, its voltage is doubled, but its amperage is cut in half.

Thus, a current can have its characteristics transformed in the process of induction. Faraday's two coils on an iron ring is the simplest version of our modern "transformers."

Faraday lived on for 35 years, working and lecturing. At Christmas time he gave many series of lectures for young people. His lectures on the candle have been collected in a book, *The Chemical History of the Candle*, which may be found in most libraries. His three-volume *Experimental Researches* may also be found in many libraries. These are the notebooks in which his discoveries are recorded. They make interesting reading.

Faraday made many contributions to science. There is scarcely an area of modern physics that does not have its starting point in his work. However, when he died on August 25, 1867, there was no doubt that his greatest discovery was that of electrical induction. His greatest inventions were the generator and the transformer.

The importance of his discovery was just this: It offered the first practical method of turning mechanical energy into electrical energy.

Before Faraday's time, there had been steam engines and waterwheels. They produced mechanical energy in large amounts out of burning coal and falling water. How-

ever, these were large in size. They could serve mills on
the spot, but not homes and offices.

There were sources of electricity before Faraday, in
the form of chemical batteries. These could supply only
small amounts of current.

Faraday's discovery of electromagnetic induction pointed the way to the production of electricity in generators turned by the mechanical energy of steam or falling water. He made it possible for the Industrial Revolution to flow out of the factory and, in the form of electricity, into the home.

The politician who supposedly questioned the value of electromagnetism would indeed be astonished at the amount of taxes collected today from company and consumer as a result of the use of this current.

Joseph Henry

Electricity Becomes Power

11

ONE of the most dramatic moments in the history of American invention came on May 24, 1844.

Wires had been strung from Baltimore to Washington, a distance of 44 miles. At one end, Samuel F. B. Morse, an artist turned inventor, pressed and released a key that closed and opened an electric circuit. He pressed it in a pattern of dots and dashes that represented the letters of the alphabet. Forty-four miles away, a small iron bar rose and fell in the exact pattern in which the key was pressed and released. The pattern of long and short clicks framed a message: "What hath God wrought?"

The telegraph was born.

Morse is to be given credit. He worked for years trying to make the telegraph practical. He traveled over Europe trying to get patents. He endured discouragement and disappointment while trying to get Congress to appropriate money for experiments.

But he does not really deserve credit for inventing the telegraph. Years before, Joseph Henry had constructed the same instrument.

Joseph Henry was born in Albany, New York, on December 17, 1797. This was six years after the birth of Michael Faraday in England. Henry's life paralleled that of Faraday closely.

Like Faraday, Henry was born of a poor family. Like Faraday, he had little schooling and was forced to go to work while young. Where Faraday was apprenticed to a bookbinder, Henry, at 13, was apprenticed to a watchmaker. In this, Henry was the less fortunate, for he didn't have Faraday's association with books. At least, he might not have had, except for an odd happening.

The story goes that at 16, while Henry was on vacation at a relative's farm, he chased a rabbit under a church building. Some of the floorboards were missing and Henry abandoned the rabbit to explore the church.

Henry found a shelf of books. One was on natural history. In curiosity, he began leafing through the book. It took as little as that to fire him with ambition. He returned to school.

He entered the Albany Academy, graduated, taught at country schools, and tutored on the side to support himself. He was all set to study medicine when an offer of a job as a surveyor turned him toward engineering. By 1826, he was teaching mathematics and science at Albany Academy.

He began to work on electricity and magnetism, and

there his life began to parallel Faraday's even more closely. Henry discovered the principle of electromagnetic induction independently of Faraday. He probably discovered self-induction, too, ahead of Faraday. (Self-induction is voltage induced in a coil, or a straight wire, just after the current in that wire is shut off. This electrical "drag" is caused by the collapse of the magnetic field that accompanies the current.) However, Faraday published his discovery first, so he gets the credit.

Then Henry branched off from Faraday's line of investigation. He began to specialize in the magnetism formed by electric currents. In 1820, the Danish physicist, Hans Christian Oersted, had shown that a coil of wire through which a current was flowing developed the properties of a magnet. In 1825, a British shoemaker named William Sturgeon, with an interest in electricity as a hobby, wrapped eighteen turns of bare copper wire around a bar of soft iron bent into a horseshoe. When current flowed through the wire the iron acted as a magnet. Sturgeon invented the name "electromagnet" for this device.

Sturgeon's device was only a toy. In 1829, however, Joseph Henry heard of it. He made the toy extremely important. He wrapped turn upon turn upon turn of wire around the iron bar. To force the current to flow through the full length of the wire and not skip from one turn of wire to the next, he wrapped the entire length of the wire in silk, insulating it.

Each turn of wire strengthened the magnet. In 1831, at Princeton, using current from an ordinary battery, he was able to lift 750 pounds of iron with an electromagnet! The same year he lifted over a ton of iron at Yale.

But electromagnets were more than a matter of brute strength. Henry built small delicate ones that could be used for fine control. Suppose you connected such an electromagnet to a mile of wire, which was also connected to a battery. Suppose you could send a current through the wire by pressing a key and closing the circuit. With the current flowing, the electromagnet, a mile away, could be made to attract a small iron bar. If you then released the key and broke the current, the electromagnet would no longer be a magnet. The iron bar would be released. By opening and closing the key in a particular pattern, you could make the distant iron bar rise and fall in the same pattern. By 1831, Henry was doing just this.

But electricity gets weak when it flows through a long length of wire. So Henry invented the "relay." A current just strong enough to activate an electromagnet would have just enough power to lift a small iron key. This key, when lifted, would close a second circuit with a much stronger current flowing through it. The second current could then activate a second electromagnet that could do the work the first couldn't have done.

But Henry did not patent his electromagnets. He believed the laws of science and their benefits belonged to all humanity and should not be used for the profit of an individual. That made it possible for inventors to use his electromagnet freely to construct gadgets which they patented.

Morse, for instance, patented his electromagnet telegraph, which worked on the same principles that Henry's did. In fact, when others tried to use Morse's telegraph without permission from him, they justified themselves by

saying that Henry had invented it anyway, not Morse. However, the courts finally ruled for Morse.

Alexander Graham Bell used a small electromagnet in his telephone. Bell's invention would have been impossible without Henry's discoveries.

In 1829, Henry used his electromagnets to cause a disc to rotate rapidly between magnetic poles when the current was turned on, and in 1831 he described this device. This was the opposite of a generator such as Faraday had invented. In a generator, a turning wheel converted mechanical force into electricity. In Henry's device, a turning wheel was used to convert electricity into mechanical force. Henry had invented the first "motor."

Both Henry's electromagnets and Henry's motor are used to this day with very little real change.

In December, 1846, Henry became the first secretary of the Smithsonian Institution, just formed in Washington with funds left by Smithson, an Englishman. This opened a new phase of Henry's life, for he became a scientific administrator. He was first-class here, too. He made the institution a clearing house of scientific knowledge, encouraging scientific communication from world's end to world's end. Henry was an American man of science with an international reputation, the first of his type since Benjamin Franklin.

He also encouraged the growth of new sciences within the United States. For instance, he was interested in meteorology, the science of weather and weather prediction. He used the resources of the Smithsonian Institution to set up a system for obtaining weather reports from all over the nation. (He was the first to use the telegraph — which he himself had made possible — for this purpose.) As a result of his example, the United States Weather Bureau was founded.

Most of us think of scientific warfare as a development of the twentieth century. However, even during the Civil War, the government was aware of the importance of science. It was Joseph Henry who headed the scientific mobilization of the Civil War.

Henry seems to have spent most of his life watching
others get credit: Faraday for induction, Morse for the
telegraph, Bell for the telephone. Even in the case of the
Weather Bureau, someone else, Cleveland Abbe, was
eventually given the credit as the "father of the Weather
Bureau."

But he was not entirely unappreciated. When Henry

died in Washington, on May 13, 1878, his funeral was attended by high government officials, including President Rutherford B. Hayes. When the International Electrical Congress met in Chicago in 1893, Henry was officially recognized as the discoverer of self-induction. It was officially decided then to measure amounts of inductance in a unit to be called a "henry" in his honor. This is still done to this day.

Faraday's discoveries made possible the production of cheap electricity, which transferred the Industrial Revolution from the factory to the home.

However, even though electricity might be led into homes in all the amounts you could imagine, there would be little for it to do there without Henry's electromagnets and motors. The energy of the motor makes possible refrigerators, washers, dryers, mixers, electric typewriters, electric sewing-machines, electric almost-anything-that-involves-moving-parts.

Sometimes it is the electromagnet alone. It pulls a piece of metal to control an electric circuit, to give us telephones, and so on.

Faraday's breakthrough supplied us with electricity. Henry's breakthrough supplied us with instruments and tools that could be run by electricity. Both men were the fathers of the gadgets which fill our homes today to make our lives and our leisure more meaningful.

Henry Bessemer

The Steel Age Opens

12

Henry bessemer had invented a new kind of projectile. It could rotate in flight and would enable a cannon to shoot farther and more accurately than had ever been possible before.

Napoleon III, new emperor of France, became interested in the invention. He offered to finance further experiments. Bessemer (an Englishman, but the son of a Frenchman) was willing, but the new projectile would need guns made out of better material than the cast iron then available. Cast iron guns would blow up under the great explosive pressure needed to fire the new projectile.

Bessemer knew nothing about the manufacture of iron, but he was determined to learn. Thus, in 1854 an age came to an end and a new age began.

Henry Bessemer, who was born in England on January 19, 1813, had already made a number of inventions. But they were only gadgets compared to the job he was about to tackle.

For two thousand years and more, men had been using iron as the hardest and strongest of the common metals.

This metal was obtained by heating iron ores with coke and limestone. The iron that resulted contained a large amount of carbon (from the coke) and was called "cast iron." It was cheap and hard, but it was brittle. A sharp blow could crack it.

Carbon could be removed from cast iron by mixing it with additional iron ore. The oxygen in the iron ore combined with the carbon in the cast iron to form carbon monoxide gas, which bubbled out and burned off. Only the almost pure iron, from the iron ore and the cast iron, was left behind. This resulting iron was called "wrought iron." This form of iron was tough and could take numerous blows and shocks without cracking. But it was quite soft, and it was expensive.

However, there was a form of iron that was half-way between cast iron and wrought iron. This was "steel." Steel could be made stronger than cast iron and harder than wrought iron, and it combined the virtues of both. Before Bessemer's time, cast iron had first to be converted to wrought iron. Then the right ingredients to make steel had to be added. If wrought iron was expensive, steel was doubly so. Steel was a rather rare metal, therefore used mainly for such things as swords.

The task Bessemer gave himself was to remove carbon from cast iron cheaply. Well, what was the cheapest

and easiest way of adding oxygen to molten iron in order
to burn off the carbon? How about a blast of air, rather
than the addition of iron ore? But wouldn't the air cool
the molten iron and solidify it?

Bessemer began experimenting. He soon proved that
the air blast would work. The air burned out the carbon
and most of the other impurities, and the heat of the
burning *raised* the temperature of the iron. By controlling
the blast, Bessemer was able to make steel at a fraction of
the cost of previous methods.

In 1856, Bessemer announced the details of his method. Iron-makers were enthusiastic. They invested fortunes in "blast furnaces" to manufacture steel the new way. Imagine their horror when they found their product was very poor grade. They heaped Bessemer with abuse. He returned to his experimenting.

It turned out that iron ore which contained phosphorus could not be used in this method. The phosphorus remained behind and made the steel brittle. In his experiments, Bessemer had happened to use phosphorus-free iron ore.

He announced this fact, but the iron-makers would no longer listen. They had had enough of the "crackpot." So Bessemer borrowed money and put up his own steel-works in Sheffield, England, in 1860. He imported phosphorus-free iron ore from Sweden and began to sell high-grade steel for $100 a ton less than any of his competitors. No arguing with that.

By 1870, ways were found of dealing with the phosphorus problem. This made possible the use of America's vast iron ore resources. Bessemer was knighted in 1879. He died in London, rich and famous, in 1898.

Cheap steel made possible engineering achievements that were only dreams until that time, for steel beams could be used as skeletons to support almost anything. Railroads began to span continents on steel rails. Great steel ships steamed across oceans. Suspension bridges spanned rivers. Skyscrapers began climbing upward. Tractors could be made stronger, and soon automobiles arrived, and they could have frameworks of steel. In war, too, new and stronger guns thundered while new and stronger armor-plate resisted.

The Iron Age came to an end and the Steel Age began. Today, aluminum, glass, and plastic have taken over where lightness is more important than strength. But where sheer strength is concerned, this is still the Age of Steel.

Edward Jenner

He Found a Way to Prevent Disease

13

IN JULY 1796, Europe was in turmoil. Napoleon Bona-
parte was winning his first great victories in Italy. Revolution was everywhere. Old ways were being overturned.

As if that weren't enough, an English doctor named
Edward Jenner was doing what seemed a monstrous thing.
He was deliberately trying to give the horrible disease of
smallpox to an eight-year-old boy. Taking clear fluid
from the blisters of a victim of smallpox, he scratched the
fluid into the skin of the boy. This should have made it
certain that the boy would soon come down with smallpox.

Jenner waited to see what would happen. With great
relief he realized that his expectations were correct. The
boy did *not* get smallpox. He showed no signs of sickness
at all.

Jenner was no monster, but a benefactor of mankind.
He had proved he knew how to prevent smallpox. In so
doing, he influenced human destiny to a far greater extent
than did Napoleon, with all his victories.

Perhaps Napoleon realized this. In 1802 a number of
English civilians were held as prisoners, after war between

England and France had broken out following a short peace. Napoleon was petitioned to release them. He was about to refuse when he learned that Edward Jenner was one of the petitioners. The would-be conqueror of Europe dared not refuse the conqueror of smallpox. The Englishmen were released.

Edward Jenner was born in Gloucestershire, England, on May 17, 1749. At the age of twenty he began to study medicine, but, as was true of so many pioneers in science, he dabbled in many things. He studied geology, wrote poetry, played musical instruments, was interested in birds, built a balloon. Fortunately for the world, though, he turned down a chance at a really glamorous job. He could have gone with Captain Cook on that explorer's second voyage into the South Seas, as official naturalist for the expedition. He chose to remain in England and practice medicine.

One of the great problems of medicine in those days was smallpox, one of the most dreaded of the diseases that afflicted mankind. Every once in a while, an epidemic of smallpox would strike. Because there was very little knowledge of hygiene, the disease spread like wildfire through the crowded, dirty cities.

As many as ten per cent of the people who caught the disease died. What's more, the victims who survived were "pock-marked." That is, each little blister caused by the disease (and in severe cases the body was covered by them) left a puckered, pitted scar after it was gone. Many people dreaded the horrible disfigurement of the disease more than they did the chance of death.

Smallpox was no respecter of persons. In 1751 George Washington contracted smallpox. He recovered, but his face was permanently scarred as a result. In 1774 King Louis XV of France contracted smallpox. He died.

In fact, an unscarred face was almost a rarity. To have a clear complexion was enough to make a woman beautiful just by contrast with most others not so fortunate.

To be sure, one dose of smallpox was all anyone could ever have. A person who had never had the disease caught it easily, if he were exposed to an active case. Once he had caught smallpox and recovered, however, he did not catch it again no matter how much he was exposed. He was "immune."

In 1718 this fact gave rise to what seemed at the time a wild story. An English noblewoman, Lady Mary Wortley Montagu, returned from a trip to Turkey and reported that the Turks had a habit of deliberately inoculating themselves with fluid taken from mild versions of the disease. The person inoculated would then get a mild case of smallpox and become immune at a cheap price. Lady Mary had enough faith in this notion to inoculate her own children.

Lady Mary, although a brilliant woman, was a kind of social butterfly, however. It was hard to take her seriously, and doctors didn't. Besides, it was difficult to convince Englishmen at that time that Turks could do anything at all that was worth imitating.

Once Jenner started practicing medicine, he became interested in smallpox. Perhaps he had heard of Lady Mary's story, and perhaps he had not. What he certainly did hear of, however, was an old "superstition" widespread in his native Gloucestershire — that there was an "enmity" between cowpox (a disease that affected cattle and could be caught by humans) and smallpox. People who got one, said the Gloucestershire farmers with a wise nod of the head, did not get the other.

Was this really superstition, Jenner wondered. After all, it was traditional for milkmaids to be beautiful. There was a vogue in France at that time for plays that featured beautiful milkmaids and shepherdesses. Was this because milkmaids, rarely scarred by smallpox, had clear complexions? Was that because in their association with cows they caught cowpox instead?

Jenner began to observe domestic animals closely.

There was a disease of horses called "the grease," in which there was a swelling and blistering in part of the leg. People working in stables and barnyards treated the blisters, then went on to milk cows. Pretty soon, the cow had cowpox. After that the man (or woman) might have a few blisters. These were usually on the hands — which handled the cow — and never on the face, where disfigurement was most feared. Furthermore, people handling domestic animals as a profession did, indeed, seem to escape smallpox.

Jenner decided that the grease and cowpox were a form of smallpox. He reasoned that by passing through an animal the disease became greatly weakened. The farmers were right. A few blisters of cowpox on the hands, and one need never worry about death or disfigurement from smallpox.

On May 14, 1796, Jenner had enough confidence in his

theory to undertake a frightful responsibility. He found a milkmaid who had cowpox. Jenner took the fluid from a blister on her hand and injected it into a boy. Two months later he inoculated the boy again, not with cowpox, but with the real thing — smallpox! The boy did not become ill. He was immune!

Of course, Jenner wanted to try it again, to make sure. It took him two years to find someone with active cowpox. During that time he must have gone nearly mad with impatience. However, he did not publish his results prematurely, but waited. In 1798 he found his cowpox at last, repeated the experiment with another patient, and again it worked. Now Jenner could publish his results

and tell the world there was a way to defeat smallpox.

The Latin word for "cow" is "vacca"; the Latin for "cowpox" is "vaccinia." Jenner coined the word "vaccination" to describe his use of cowpox inoculation to create immunity to smallpox.

So careful was Jenner's work that only a few conservative doctors objected. Harm was done by eager ones who had began to inoculate carelessly and spread severe infections. Vaccination spread to all parts of Europe.

The British royal family was vaccinated. A Royal Jennerian Society (headed by Jenner) was founded in 1803 to encourage vaccination. In 18 months, the number of deaths from smallpox was reduced by two thirds.

In Germany, where Jenner's birthday is celebrated as a holiday, the state of Bavaria made vaccination compulsory in 1807. Other nations followed. Even backward Russia adopted the practice. The first child to be vaccinated there was named Vaccinov and was educated at the expense of the nation.

England was slowest to honor Jenner. In 1813, for instance, he was proposed for election to the College of Physicians in London. The college, however, wanted to test him in the "classics"; that is, in the theories of Hippocrates and Galen. Jenner refused. He thought his victory over smallpox was enough to qualify him. The gentlemen of the college did not agree with Jenner. He was not elected.

He died on January 24, 1823, without the membership, but with all the glory a doctor could have.

Smallpox is now a rare disease, thanks to vaccination. In most countries every child is vaccinated at an early age. If there is even a single case of smallpox in some city (brought in usually by ship from some backward region), there is at once a drive to vaccinate everyone in the city again, so that an epidemic has no chance to start.

But that is only a small part of it. Jenner had discovered a way to prevent a disease, rather than to cure one — the first man to do this. He did it by using the body's own machinery to develop immunity. Thus he founded the science of immunology.

Ever since, doctors have been tracking down new ways of encouraging the body to develop immunity to dangerous diseases, by getting it to manufacture chemical defenses ("antibodies") against mild versions of the disease. The fluids that cause the mild disease are still called "vaccines," though they have nothing to do with cows.

A recent example is the Salk vaccine, developed by Dr. Jonas Salk. The virus that causes infantile paralysis is killed by chemicals, so that it can no longer cause the disease. It still retains enough of its original properties, however, to cause the body to produce antibodies which will be effective against the living virus. Injection of the Salk vaccine increases immunity to infantile paralysis without putting you through the disease itself.

Vaccination also helps fight such diseases as yellow fever, typhoid fever, influenza, tuberculosis, and Rocky Mountain spotted fever.

The importance of Jenner's work is not just that it wiped out smallpox. It pointed out a pathway to wipe out other of man's most dreaded diseases — a pathway which may, in time, be used to ward off all infectious diseases.

Louis Pasteur

He Tracked Down the Killers

14

LOUIS PASTEUR was born on December 27, 1822. He did not shine as a student in his early school days. In college he did only moderately well in chemistry. It was only after graduation, when he attended the lectures of Jean B. Dumas, a great French chemist, that he was fired with ambition. It was not until then that he decided to devote his life to science.

Pasteur began his research by studying two chemicals — tartaric acid and racemic acid. These chemicals seemed to be alike in every respect but one: tartaric acid had an odd, twisting effect on certain kinds of light; racemic acid did not have this effect.

Pasteur's friends laughed at him. Why worry about a little thing like that? But Pasteur did worry. He obtained crystals of both acids and studied them under a microscope. The crystals of tartaric acid were all identical. Those of racemic acid were of two types. One type looked like crystals of tartaric acid; crystals of the other type were mirror images of the first. (It was like looking at a pile of gloves, some right-hand gloves and some left-hand.)

With infinite patience, Pasteur separated the racemic acid crystals into two piles. The crystals that looked like tartaric acid crystals twisted light just as tartaric acid did. The other crystals also twisted light, but in the opposite direction.

Pasteur had discovered that molecules could be "right-handed" or "left-handed." Eventually this discovery led to a revolutionary new understanding concerning the structure of the important chemicals that make up living tissue.

Pasteur's achievement received immediate recognition, although he was only 26 at the time. He was elected to membership in France's distinguished Legion of Honor.

In 1854 Pasteur became dean of the Faculty of Sciences at the University of Lille, in the heart of the vineyard country. There he became interested in the problems of France's important wine industry. Wine and beer often went sour as it aged. Millions of francs were lost as a result. Wasn't there some chemical that could be added to prevent this? The wine and beer people turned to the famous young chemist now in their midst.

Again Pasteur used the microscope. He looked at the dregs of good wine under the microscope, then compared them with the dregs of soured wine. Both contained yeast cells, but the shape of the cells was different. There was a special kind of yeast that soured wine.

This souring-yeast must be killed, explained Pasteur.

Once the wine or beer is formed, heat it gently at about 120° F. That will kill any yeast still left, including the souring-yeast that might have gotten in during the wine-making. After that, stopper it and there will be no souring.

The wine-makers were horrified at the thought of heating wine. Pasteur set out to convince them. He heated some samples, left others unheated, and told the wine-makers to wait a few months. When the heated samples were opened they were all fine. The unheated ones had soured in a number of cases. The wine-makers stopped objecting.

Ever since, gentle heating to kill undesirable microscopic organisms has been termed "pasteurization." It is

for this reason that we pasteurize the milk we drink.

Pasteur, in the process of this research, decided that all fermentation and decay were the work of living organisms.

People objected to this theory. After all, even if meat is boiled to kill bacteria, it will still spoil if allowed to stand.

But, said Pasteur, there are germs everywhere, and germs fall into the meat from the air.

Pasteur boiled meat extract and left it exposed to air, but the air could get in only through a long, narrow S-shaped flask neck. Dust particles (and germs) settled at the bottom of the S. The meat did not spoil. There were no germs in cooked meat. No decay took place without germs. Once and for all, Pasteur had disproved the theory of "spontaneous generation" (the belief that living organisms could originate from non-living material).

In 1865 Pasteur went to southern France to study a silk-worm disease that was threatening the entire hundred-million-franc-a-year industry.

Using his microscope again, Pasteur located a tiny parasite infesting silkworms and the mulberry leaves that were fed to them. Pasteur said: destroy the infested worms and leaves. Begin all over again with healthy worms and clean leaves and they will stay that way. It worked. The industry was saved.

Pasteur himself almost was not. He had a paralytic

stroke in 1868, and for a while thought he was going to die. Fortunately he recovered.

In 1870 France was tricked into fighting a war with Prussia. The military might of the Prussians had been steadily developing under a policy of "blood and iron." The French were caught unprepared. Louis Pasteur immediately tried to enlist. His offer was firmly refused.

"Monsieur Pasteur," the army officers told him, "you are 48 and you have had a paralytic stroke. You can serve France better outside the army."

France was disastrously defeated. The conquering Prussians imposed an indemnity of five billion francs upon the French. The Prussians thought this would keep France helpless for years to come. France astounded the world by paying the indemnity in full within a year.

Where did France get the money? From the work of Louis Pasteur, who had saved France's industries and made her prosperous.

By now the discoveries of Pasteur were beginning to make sound sense to some doctors. They asked: What about certain human ailments? Was it possible that they were caused by microscopic parasites?

In England, Joseph Lister, a surgeon, was heartsick over the fact that half his patients died of infection after surgery was successfully completed. In some other hospitals, 80 per cent of the patients died. Suppose, Lister reasoned,

he were to "pasteurize" wounds and surgical incisions.
Suppose he killed the germs in them as Pasteur killed yeast
in wine.

In 1865 Lister began to use carbolic acid on wounds.
In three years he cut the death rate after surgery by two
thirds. He had invented "antiseptic surgery." You imitate
Lister every time you put iodine on a cut.

In 1871, after the war, Pasteur came to Lister's conclusion independently. He was appalled at the death rate in
military hospitals. He forced doctors (often against their
will) to boil their instruments and steam their bandages.
Kill the germs, he insisted, kill them. And the death rate
fell.

(About 25 years earlier, an Austrian physician, Ignaz
Semmelweis, had tried to force disinfection on doctors.
Semmelweis cried out that doctors were murderers, carrying disease on their hands. He tried to get them to wash
their hands with bleaching powder solutions before ap-
proaching a patient. Semmelweis got nowhere and died
a failure in 1865 after accidentally infecting himself. He
did not live to see Lister and Pasteur prove him right.)

Pasteur gradually adopted what we now call the "germ"
theory of disease." Every infectious disease, he decided,
was caused by germs. It was infectious because germs
could be carried from one person to another. Locate the

germ, he said, find out how to fight it, and you've conquered the disease.

A German doctor, Robert Koch, developed techniques
to grow disease germs outside the body. Together he and
Pasteur learned to control disease after disease. Frenchman and German united to serve humanity. The 1880's
were the most dramatic years of Pasteur's life. He learned
to inoculate against the animal diseases of anthrax (which
killed cattle and sheep) and chicken cholera, and how to
protect man against the dread disease of mad dogs —
hydrophobia.

Dramatic as these were, they were only the natural consequence of the germ theory of disease, and it was Pasteur's early work which led to that. When Pasteur died on September 28, 1895, modern medicine had become a reality.

The germ theory of disease was probably the greatest single medical discovery in history. Once the germ theory was adopted, disease could be fought systematically. Drinking water could be boiled or chemically treated; sewage-disposal became a science; sterile procedures were developed in hospitals and in the commercial preparation of food; disinfectants and germ-killers were developed; germ-carriers such as mosquitoes and rats were fought relentlessly.

In country after country, as these things were done, the death rate fell and life expectancy rose. In 1850 the life expectancy of the American male was 38 years; now it is 68. Thank Louis Pasteur and his fellow scientists for some of those 30 years.

Gregor Johann Mendel

The Mystery of Heredity

15

In 1900 three strangers met at a crossroads of research. Each, without knowledge of the other two, had worked out the rules that govern inheritance of physical characteristics by living things. The three were Hugo de Vries of Holland, Carl Correns of Germany, and Erich Tschermak of Austria-Hungary.

Each made ready to announce his discovery to the world. In preparation, each looked through previous issues of various scientific journals, to check earlier work in the field. Each, to his astonishment, found an amazing paper by someone named Gregor Johann Mendel in a 35-year-old copy of an obscure publication. Mendel, in 1865, had observed all the phenomena that the three scientists were preparing to report in 1900.

Each made the same decision. With an honesty that is one of the glories of scientific history, each abandoned his own claims and called attention to Mendel's discovery. Each man advanced his own work only as confirmation.

Gregor Johann Mendel was born of peasant parents in 1822. He lived his life quietly and uneventfully — except for his great discovery — as a monk, and later an abbott, in an Augustinian monastery in Bruenn, Austria. (The city is now called Brno and is part of Czechoslovakia.)

Mendel had two hobbies, statistics and gardening, a combination he put to good use. For eight years, starting in 1857, he raised peas. Carefully, Mendel self-pollinated various plants, making sure that the seeds which were thus produced would inherit characteristics from only one parent. Carefully, he saved the seeds produced by each self-pollinated pea plant, planted them separately, and studied the new generation.

He found that if he planted seeds from dwarf pea plants, only dwarf pea plants sprouted. The seeds produced by this second generation also produced only dwarf pea plants. The dwarf pea plants "bred true."

Seeds from tall pea plants did not always behave in quite this way. Some tall pea plants (about a third of those in his garden) did breed true, producing tall pea plants generation after generation. The majority, however, did not. Of these, the seeds of some produced tall plants, and the seeds of others produced dwarf plants. There were always about three times as many tall plants produced by these seeds as dwarf plants.

Apparently, then, there were two kinds of tall pea plants, the true-breeders and the non-true-breeders.

Mendel then went a step further. He cross-bred dwarf

plants with true-breeding tall plants. Now the seeds would be the product of two unlike parents. What would happen? Would the offspring be some dwarf and some tall?

No, indeed. Every resulting "hybrid" seed produced a tall plant! The characteristic of dwarfness seemed to have disappeared.

Next Mendel self-pollinated each hybrid plant and studied the results. They were all of the non-true-breeding type. One quarter of the seeds developed into true-breeding dwarf plants. One quarter developed into true-breeding tall plants. One half developed into non-true-breeding tall plants.

Apparently, non-true-breeding tall plants contain within themselves the characteristics of both tallness and dwarfness. When the two characteristics were both present, only tallness showed; it was "dominant." Dwarfness, however, although "recessive" and not visible, was still there. It showed up in the next generation.

Mendel thus had his "first law of inheritance." He also studied the inheritance of other characteristics and developed further rules.

But he was only an amateur and could not interest any important scientists in his work. He published his paper in a small local journal and no one paid attention. It lay unnoticed for 35 years.

Mendel died in 1884 without continuing his work, which had ended in 1865, or living to see his work recognized.

The science founded by Mendel is now called "genetics." It is still a young science, and much remains to be learned about it. Careful studies of how certain physical abnormalities are inherited will help doctors, someday, in advising for or against certain marriages. It will help them to be prepared for the likely occurrence of a disease such as diabetes in a particular individual.

Genetics points to the past as well as the future. Study of the patterns of inherited blood groups gives hints of the routes taken in the migrations of primitive man.

The genetics of micro-organisms has also developed a unique importance. The manner of inheritance of the ability to perform certain chemical syntheses in various molds and bacteria, has enlightened biochemists as to the exact routes by which certain body chemicals are formed. It is for work of this sort that Drs. G. M. Beadle and E. L. Tatum recently received a Nobel Prize.

William Henry Perkin

He Opened Wide a Chemical Wonderland

16

IN 1856, when William Henry Perkin was only eighteen, a casual remark sent him off on an impossible task. Out of his failure at that task, he snatched fame for himself and gave the world an Aladdin's lamp of chemical wonders.

At that time, young Perkin was assistant to a German chemist, A. W. von Hofmann. Hofmann had been invited to England eleven years earlier to establish a center for teaching chemistry and carrying on research. Hofmann was then chiefly interested in two things. First, he was fascinated by the chemicals in coal tar, a sticky black substance one could obtain by heating coal in the absence of air. Coal tar was a mixture of complex organic substances out of which the chemist could build new compounds. Second, Hofmann was interested in applying chemistry to medicine.

After all, Hofmann wondered aloud one day, why could not quinine, the medicine used to battle malaria, be formed from the chemicals in coal tar. There would then be no need to import quinine from South America.

Perkin's interest lit up. He obtained coal tar chemicals

and began to experiment with them in the laboratory he had set up in his home. Perkin did not know that to prepare quinine from coal tar chemicals was impossible with the chemical knowledge available at that time. Of course, he got nowhere in his impossible task.

One day, after he had mixed aniline (one of the coal tar chemicals) and potassium dichromate, and was about to pour out the usual mess in his beaker, he stopped. Was that a purplish glint at the bottom of the gunk? He added alcohol to see whether he could dissolve anything out of the mess. The alcohol turned a beautiful purple.

The first artificial dye had been discovered. Perkin, purely by accident, had opened a world of color.

William Henry Perkin was born in London on March

12, 1838. His father, who was a builder, wanted his son to follow in his own footsteps. At 14, however, young William watched a friend perform experiments in chemistry. That was it. He knew what his life work would be.

History repeated itself. Once the great scientist Michael Faraday had found youthful inspiration in attending the lectures of Humphrey Davy. Now William Perkin found the same kind of inspiration in attending the lectures of Michael Faraday.

In those days English educators had a low opinion of chemistry. City schools taught the subject only during the lunch recess, not expecting many students to be interested. The Royal College of Science had a fairly good course in chemistry only because it had imported Hofmann.

By the time Perkin was 17, however, he had shown himself so capable at the Royal College that Hofmann took him on as an assistant. The next year Perkin discovered his purple substance.

Perkin's sharp mind saw at once that the substance had a possible use as a dye. In 1856 blue indigo (obtained from the indigo plant) and red alizarin (from the root of the madder plant) were the chief dyes. There were practically no others that would hold firmly to textiles without being washed out or faded by exposure to sun and weather.

A friend suggested to Perkin that he send a sample of his material to a firm in Scotland interested in dyes. Would this stuff do? he asked.

Yes, came back the excited answer, provided it could be produced cheaply.

Perkin now reached a decision that took courage and faith. He patented his process for making the dye, which he called Aniline Purple. Then he left school and became a businessman. Hofmann objected, but Perkin went his own way stubbornly.

What Perkin needed most was money. He could raise none from bankers, for who would listen to a teen-ager who wanted to make color out of coal? However, Perkin's father and elder brother tossed their life savings into the venture. In 1857 the Perkin family started to build their dye factory.

They had to start from scratch in every way. First they had to get aniline, for there was scarcely any available. It had few uses in 1857.

So Perkin had to buy benzene (also derived from coal tar) at an exorbitant price and make aniline out of it. To do this, he needed strong nitric acid. He couldn't get any strong enough, so he had to make his own from Chile saltpeter and sulfuric acid. At every step of the game, Perkin needed special equipment to carry out the necessary chemical reactions. None existed and he had to design his own. Some of the equipment used in the manufacture of dyes today still follows Perkin's original designs.

Finally he began producing Aniline Purple.

Fortune then smiled. English dyers were conservative, as Englishmen usually are, but the French dyers went for it in a big way. The color resembled the color of the petals of a flower whose official name is "Malva sylvestris," so the French called the color "mauve." They used the color in their new fashions. Paris, then as now, was the center of the fashion world. Mauve became the rage. Perkin's factory sold all the dye it could turn out. The young chemist found himself suddenly rich and famous.

When he was still only 23, Perkin was the world authority on dyes, and he lectured on them before London's Chemical Society. Michael Faraday himself was in the audience. Teacher and student had changed places.

Chemists in other countries now entered the new field of synthetic dyes. Hofmann, Perkin's teacher, returned to Germany in 1865 and became professor of organic chemistry at the University of Berlin. Hofmann, too, began to investigate dyes (as Perkin's student, in a way). Although England had been first in the field, she could not hold out against Germany's greater over-all achievements in organic chemistry. This is the branch of chemistry which deals with compounds of carbon, which are typically found in living organisms.

While Perkin was active in business, the race between the two countries was fairly even. For instance, German chemists worked out the chemical structure of alizarin, the most famous of the natural dyes. Now there began a race to find a way of making it cheaply in the laboratory. Perkin solved the problem in 1869 and applied for a patent.

The German chemists solved the problem at about the same time. They applied for a patent one day sooner. Nevertheless, Perkin manufactured alizarin in quantities by arrangement with the Germans. Again his factory prospered.

Ten years later the Germans synthesized indigo. This time there was no battle. The Germans were in control. They remained the dye-makers of the world until World War I.

In 1874 Perkin, then only 35, was independently

wealthy. He sold his factory and turned to his first love, chemical research.

His career in research was also fruitful. In 1875 he synthesized coumarin, a substance that had a pleasant odor. This pointed the way to the synthetic perfume industry.

Honors of all sorts were showered on Perkin, but the climax came in 1906, the fiftieth anniversary of his discovery of Aniline Purple. He was knighted, then honored at special gatherings in Europe and America. In New York the Perkin Medal was founded in his honor, to be given to those who made important contributions to applied chemistry. At these dinners ties were worn which

had been dyed with the original batch of Aniline Purple. Some of these ties still exist, treasured by winners of the Perkin Medal.

Perkin died the next year, on July 14, 1907. Life before him was largely colorless. Good dyes in ancient times had been rare. The city of Tyre owed its prosperity to a secret method for making a purple dye out of a species of snail. This "Tyrian Purple" was so expensive that it was used only by the very rich. At the time of the Byzantine Empire, only the emperor could use it. From this comes our expression "born to the purple."

Perkin found the world drab; he left it colorful. Thousands of dyes of every shade and tint have been discovered since Perkin showed the way. Almost anyone today can dress in colors so numerous and brilliant as to put a Roman emperor to shame.

More important, Perkin's work showed the world that a substance manufactured in the test tube did not have to be a mere imitation, a poor substitute for the real thing found in nature. Synthetics, he showed, could *improve* on nature. Synthetic dyes put natural dyes out of business, not just because the synthetics were cheaper, but because they were *better*.

Success in the chemical synthesis of dyes led to renewed efforts in other fields. Today synthetics range all the way from fabrics and rubber to drugs and chemical additives to make our food more wholesome and palatable. During World War II chemists produced even a substitute for quinine to treat malaria — as if finally to vindicate Perkin in his "impossible" task.

Today the chemist redesigns nature — boldly and confidently.

Roentgen and Becquerel

They Discovered Invisible Rays

17

Professor WILHELM ROENTGEN was fascinated by the mysterious illumination that resulted when electricity was discharged in a tube from which all the air had been pumped.

The eerie illumination inside the tube seemed to start at the negative electrode, or "cathode," so the phenomenon was referred to as "cathode rays." When the rays hit the glass of the tube, the glass glowed with a greenish light. Certain chemicals placed near the tube glowed (or "luminesced") even more brilliantly than did the glass.

Roentgen was particularly interested in the *luminescence.* On November 5, 1895, he enclosed his cathode ray tube in a box made of thin, black cardboard and darkened the room. Thus he would be able to observe the luminescence without the interference of outside light.

He turned on the electricity. Almost at once a flash of light that did not come from the tube caught his eye. He looked up. Quite a distance from the tube, he happened to have a sheet of paper coated with barium platinocyanide. He used the paper in his experiments because barium platinocyanide was one of the chemicals that glowed when placed near the cathode ray tube.

But why should it be glowing *now?* The tube was in a cardboard box.

Roentgen turned off the electricity. The coated paper became dark. He turned on the electricity again. The paper glowed once more. He walked into the next room with the coated paper, closed the door, and pulled down the blinds. The paper continued to glow while the tube was in operation.

He had discovered something invisible that was "felt"

through cardboard and closed doors. Years later another scientist, meeting Roentgen, asked about that experience.

"What did you think?" he wanted to know.

Roentgen answered, "I didn't think. I experimented."

Of course, Roentgen was giving a flip answer. He did think — very deeply.

Wilhelm Conrad Roentgen was born on March 27, 1845, in Lennep, a small town in the Ruhr section of western Germany. For most of his early life, however, he lived outside Germany. He received his primary education in Holland, and went to college in Zurich, Switzerland.

It was only after he had finished college that he discovered his life work. In 1868 he was graduated from college with a degree in mechanical engineering. When he decided to go on for advanced degrees in Zurich, he came under the influence of a well-known physicist, August Kundt. Under him, Roentgen became interested in physics and received his Ph.D. in that subject. For six years thereafter, teacher and student worked together.

Kundt accepted positions in Germany. Roentgen accompanied him. Soon he was teaching and doing research on his own.

Roentgen rose steadily in his profession. In 1888 a new institute of physics was opened at the University of Wurzburg in Bavaria. Roentgen was invited to head it. It was there that he discovered his penetrating rays and won world fame.

The mysterious rays that caused chemicals to luminesce through cardboard and doors were called "Roentgen rays" in honor of the discoverer. Roentgen himself, in honor of their unknown nature, gave his rays the mathematical symbol for the unknown. He called them "X rays." That is their common name.

Roentgen experimented vigorously. He found what thicknesses of various materials could be penetrated by X rays. He discovered that they would fog a photographic plate, just as sunlight would. He published his results on December 28, 1895. The scientific world was amazed.

A number of scientists found that they had encountered these mysterious rays. William Crookes, a British scientist who had worked with cathode rays, had noticed several times that photographic films nearby had become fogged. He had thought it accidental and paid no attention. In 1890 an American physicist, A. W. Goodspeed, had actually produced what we now call an X-ray photograph, but he was not sufficiently interested to follow it up and prove the nature of the phenomenon.

Roentgen's work caught the imagination of a French scientist, Henri Antoine Becquerel, seven years younger than Roentgen. Becquerel was the son of an eminent scientist. Becquerel's father had been interested in a type of luminescence called "fluorescence." Fluorescent materials glowed upon exposure to ultra-violet light or to sunlight, which contains ultra-violet rays.

Becquerel wondered: Could this fluorescence have any mysterious X rays in it? In February 1896, Becquerel wrapped photographic film in black paper, put it in sunlight, and put a crystal of a fluorescent chemical upon the paper. He used a chemical his father had been particularly interested in, a uranium compound.

Sure enough, when the film was developed it was found to be fogged. Ordinary sunlight would not have passed through the black paper, but X rays could. Becquerel decided the uranium salt was giving off X rays as it fluoresced.

Then came a series of cloudy days and Becquerel could not continue his experiments. By March 1 he was restless. His wrapped photographic plates and his crystals remained in the drawer. He decided to develop some of the films anyway. Perhaps a little of the original fluorescence persisted. Perhaps there would be some faint fogging, even though the crystals hadn't been exposed to sunlight for days. At least it was something to do.

Imagine his amazement when he found the film fogged as strongly as ever. He quickly found that exposure to sun was unnecessary. Uranium salts gave off a radiation constantly, one even more penetrating than X rays.

By 1897 the nature of the cathode rays was established. J. J. Thomson, an English physicist, showed that the rays consisted of tiny particles speeding at breakneck velocities. What's more, these particles were much smaller than atoms. They were the first "sub-atomic particles" to be discovered, and were called "electrons."

When these electrons smashed into atoms, they released energy in a form that did indeed resemble ordinary light, except that it was more energetic and more penetrating. Thus, when these speeding electrons (or cathode rays) struck the anode in a cathode ray tube, X rays were produced. These X rays were part of the electromagnetic spectrum, of which visible light is another part.

As for Becquerel's uranium rays, these proved to consist of three parts. The most penetrating part, called gamma radiation, was similar to X rays but more energetic. The rest of the radiation was made up of electrons and helium nuclei.

A complete revolution took place in physics. Before 1896 the atom had been considered a tiny, unsplittable particle, the smallest portion of matter. Suddenly it was found to be made up of still smaller particles with strange properties. Some atoms, such as those of uranium, actually broke up into simpler atoms, all by themselves.

This proof that atoms disintegrate and emit electrons

opened a great new world to science. There followed 60 years of rapid advances that led to nuclear physics and exploration of the atom.

Roentgen's discovery, from the standpoint of pure science, was supremely important. But before that became apparent to the average man, there was an immediate advance in medicine that affected almost everyone.

X rays penetrate the soft tissues of the body easily, but are largely stopped by bone and entirely stopped by metal. X rays, passing through the body to a photographic film behind, show light gray where bones stop most of them, gray and fogged in varying degree elsewhere.

Doctors found they had a way of looking into the human body quickly, easily and — above all — without cutting.

Small breaks in bones could be discovered; disorders in the joints; the beginnings of tuberculosis in lungs; foreign objects in the stomach — in short, the doctor had a kind of magic eye at his disposal. Only four days after news of Roentgen's discovery reached America, X rays were used to locate a bullet in a patient's leg. The dentist, too, had a magic eye. He could look for the beginnings of decay in teeth with Roentgen's invisible radiation.

X rays (and gamma rays) can kill living tissue, and if focussed properly can kill cancer cells which the surgeon's knife cannot reach. Today, however, we know they must be used with caution, and only when necessary.

In industry, too, X rays are used. They can detect internal flaws in the structure of metals, flaws that would be invisible otherwise. In chemistry they are used to probe the atomic structure of crystals and of complex protein molecules. In both cases, they open new windows into what was previously hidden.

Thanks to Roentgen, we can — odd though it sounds — use the invisible to make the invisible visible.

Thomas Alva Edison

Bringer of Light

18

As THE Industrial Revolution progressed in the nineteenth century, the houses and cities of the western world grew larger and more prosperous. Better light was needed during the hours of darkness. Illumination was provided by gas, but the flickering gas jets did not give enough light. The open flames also increased the danger of fire, and gas leaks could mean death.

Of course, there was the power of electricity. Everyone knew that electricity heated wires through which it passed. What if a wire could be heated to a white-hot glow? Wouldn't that serve as illumination?

Beginning about 1800, for three quarters of a century inventors tried to use electricity to produce light. Some thirty inventors or would-be inventors came, tried, and failed. The theory was plain and simple, but it seemed impossible to overcome the practical difficulties.

In 1878 Thomas Alva Edison, then 31, announced that he would tackle the problem. Instantly, the news spread around the world. So absolute was the faith in his ability, that illuminating gas stocks tumbled in value in New York and London. For Edison had just made a machine talk. He was the man whose achievements had convinced people he could invent *anything*.

Thomas A. Edison was born in Milan, Ohio, on February 11, 1847. He showed no early signs of genius. In fact, his curious way of asking questions was taken for "queerness" by the neighbors. His teacher at school told him he was "addled." Edison's mother, a former teacher, was furious. She took young Tom out of the school at once.

Tom Edison found his real school in books and in his hands. He read everything he could find on almost every subject, and his unusual mind began to show itself. He remembered almost everything he read, and he gradually learned to read almost as quickly as he could turn the pages.

When he began to read books on science, he began to experiment, too. He set up a chemical laboratory in his house, to his mother's despair. The cost of buying chemicals and equipment drove him to earning money.

First, he tried raising vegetables for sale. Then, at the age of 14, he got a job as a newsboy on a train between Port Huron and Detroit, Mich. (During the stop at Detroit, he spent his time in the library.)

His regular earnings were not enough. So he bought

second-hand printing equipment and began to publish a weekly newspaper. Soon he was selling 400 copies of each issue to the train travelers.

With the money he earned, he set up a chemical laboratory in the baggage car. There he could experiment to his heart's content. But things did not go well. Once, on a section of rough track, a jar of phosphorus fell and broke, causing a fire. It was put out, but the furious conductor boxed Edison's ears and put him and his equipment off the train. That ended that.

Edison had another misfortune in those days. Once, trying to board a moving train, he found he couldn't quite make it. He hung on wildly, in danger of falling off and being killed. A trainman pulled him up and in by his ears. Edison's life was saved, but the delicate mechanism of the inner ear was damaged. He was partly deaf the rest of his life.

In 1862 another phase of Edison's life began. Fifteen-year-old Tom spied a small boy on the train tracks, with a freight car rolling toward him. He dashed for the boy and pulled him out of harm's way. The grateful father had no money with which to reward Tom, so he offered to teach him telegraphy. That was worth more to Edison, of course, than almost any amount of money.

Edison became one of the fastest telegraph operators of his time. So automatically did he work, the story goes,

that when he received the telegraphed flash that Lincoln
had been assassinated, he took down the message mechanically, without being aware of what had happened.

In 1868 Edison went to Boston, where he got a job as a
telegrapher. The other men in the office tried to joke with
the country boy by setting him down to receive messages
from New York's fastest dot-dasher. Edison took down
with ease everything that came over the wire. They
cheered him when he finished.

That year Edison patented his first invention. It was a
device to record votes mechanically in Congress. He
thought it would speed the business of lawmaking. However, a Congressman told him that there was no desire to
speed proceedings. Sometimes a slow vote was a political
necessity. After that, Edison decided never to invent anything unless he was sure it was needed.

In 1869 he went to New York City to find employment.
While he was in a broker's office, waiting to be inter-
viewed, a telegraph machine broke down. It was a device
that reported the price of gold. Fortunes depended upon
it. Now it had suddenly stopped for no known reason.
The office was in pandemonium. None of the operators
or mechanics could find the trouble. Edison had a look at
the machine, and calmly announced he knew what was
wrong.

"Fix it. Fix it," shouted the boss wildly. Edison repaired it in a few minutes and was offered a job — a better-paying one than he had ever had before. He didn't stay long. In a few months he decided to become a professional inventor, beginning with a stock-ticker he had devised during his stay in Wall Street. It was a device to keep brokers up to date on stock prices.

Edison offered to sell the invention to the president of a large Wall Street firm. But he couldn't make up his mind whether to ask $3,000, or take a daring chance and ask for $5,000. Losing his courage, he said, "Make me an offer." The Wall Street man said, "How about $40,000?"

Edison, only 23, was in business. For the next six years Edison worked in Newark, New Jersey, turning out inventions, working about 20 hours a day, sleeping in cat naps, and developing a group of capable assistants. Somehow he found time to get married.

Lots of money came in, but to Edison money was only something to invest in more experiments.

In 1876 Edison set up a laboratory in Menlo Park, New Jersey. It was to be an "invention factory." He hoped to be able to produce a new invention every ten days. The "Wizard of Menlo Park" (as he came to be called) patented well over a thousand inventions before he died, a record no other inventor has ever approached.

In Menlo Park, Edison improved the telephone and made it workable. There he invented what proved to be his own favorite accomplishment — the phonograph. He put tinfoil on a cylinder, set a free-floating needle skimming over it, and connected a receiver to carry sound waves to and from the needle. This machine, he announced, will talk.

His own associates laughed at him, including the mechanic who had built the machine to Edison's specifications. But Edison won. He talked into the receiver while the foil-covered cylinder revolved under the needle. Then he placed the needle at the beginning of the cylinder and his own words came out at him: "Mary had a little lamb, its fleece was white as snow — "

"Gott im Himmel," cried the mechanic who had built the machine.

A machine that talked! The whole world was astonished. Edison was a wizard, indeed. So when he next announced he would invent an electric light, everyone believed him.

This time, however, Edison had bitten off almost more than he could chew. For a while it looked as though he would fail. It took him a year and $50,000 to find that platinum wires would not work.

After hundreds of experiments, Edison found what he wanted: a wire that would warm to white heat without melting or breaking. No metal was needed after all — only a scorched cotton thread; a fragile carbon filament.

On October 21, 1879, Edison set up a bulb with such
a filament. It burned for forty continuous hours. The
electric light was a reality! On the next New Year's Eve,
the main street of Menlo Park was illuminated by electricity in a public demonstration. Newspaper reporters
from all the world came to cover the event, and to marvel
at history's greatest inventor.

That was the climax of Edison's life. He never again
reached this peak, although he worked on for more than
half a century. He patented crucial inventions that made
motion pictures and the whole electronics industry pos-

sible. A stream of inventions issued out of Edison's work-shop until he died on October 18, 1931, at the age of 84.

To be sure, Edison was no scientist. He discovered only one new phenomenon — the "Edison effect." This he patented in 1883. It involved the passage of electricity from a filament to a metal plate inside an incandescent lamp globe. The discovery was not widely heralded at the time. Edison himself did not pursue it. But it made possible the radio tube and all the electronic marvels of today.

Abstract knowledge did not concern Edison. He was

a practical man, interested in arranging abstract discoveries of others into useful devices.

Nor do the devices themselves represent Edison's great contribution to our life. We enjoy the phonograph, motion pictures, the electric light, the telephone, and all the other things he made possible or practical. Still, we must admit that if he had not invented them, someone else might have, sooner or later. These things were "in the air."

But Edison did more than invent. He put invention on a mass-production basis. Before his time, people thought of inventions as being strokes of luck. Edison worked out inventions on order. He showed people that inventions were not a matter of luck or a brainstorm. Genius, he said, was one per cent inspiration and ninety-nine per cent perspiration. Inventions required hard working and hard thinking.

People came to expect invention and improvement in their daily life as a matter of course. They began to expect material progress. They began to assume that scientists, engineers, and inventors would always find new and better ways of doing things.

It is difficult to pinpoint any particular invention as Edison's breakthrough. Edison's contribution to science was the whole idea of continuous, inevitable progress — made possible by dedicated researchers working as a group or individually, to enlarge man's horizon.

Paul Ehrlich

He Fired a Magic Bullet

19

"THE antibodies," Paul Ehrlich would say, "are magic bullets, which find their target by themselves."

He was speaking of the complicated protein molecules developed by the body to neutralize the action of germs or their toxins. These "antibodies" made a person immune to certain diseases. They attacked the germs, *without* harming the body cells. The antibodies were selective, hitting the bull's-eye of their target and not damaging anything else. Magic bullets? Certainly.

But the body could not manufacture antibodies for all diseases. Certain tropical diseases caused by trypanosomes (tiny one-celled animals), such as the deadly sleeping sickness spread by the tsetse fly in Africa, could not be cured.

Ehrlich then took the next great step. He thought: If the body can't make a magic bullet, let's make one for it in the test tube!

Paul Ehrlich was born on March 14, 1854, in a small town in Germany. Even at an early age, he was interested in animals and chemicals. It is not surprising, then, that when he went to medical school, he began to explore the effect of certain chemicals on animal tissues.

In those days, only a few physicians thought of chemistry in association with medicine. Fortunately, Ehrlich's tutor at the University of Strassburg, Professor Waldeyer, was one who did. He approved Ehrlich's detailed experiments and allowed the young man to go his own way.

What interested Ehrlich most were various dyes. Chemists (beginning with Perkin) had just learned how to make them. Ehrlich was fascinated by the fact that some dyes stained tissues and some did not. Moreover, some dyes stained only certain cells and not others. Some dyes stained only certain parts of a cell and not others.

This made dyes a useful tool for biologists. For instance, certain dyes enabled Ehrlich to discover a new kind of cell. He wrote his thesis on the staining of cells by dyes.

Ehrlich's active mind passed on to something else. If particular cells could be picked out by proper staining methods, perhaps bacteria might be made more visible in this way. Perhaps some bacteria might stain more brightly than neighboring body cells. He actually found cases where some dyes did this. Ehrlich also discovered how to stain the bacterium of tuberculosis. Thus he attracted the interest of Robert Koch, the great doctor who had identified the germ. While working with the germ, though, Ehrlich caught a light case of tuberculosis. He went to Egypt to be cured by the dry climate.

Meanwhile, another German doctor, Emil von Behring, had discovered that animals produced chemicals that combine with germs in some way and make them harmless. He found that these "antibodies" were produced after the first attack of a disease. Thereafter, that animal was immune.

When Ehrlich returned from Egypt in 1889, he heard of this. At once he saw that these antibodies must work the way his dyes did. They combined with some cells and not with others.

He joined von Behring and worked up a famous "side-

chain" theory. This theory explained how antibodies were formed and how they worked.

Though most of the credit at first went to von Behring, it was Ehrlich who learned how to induce animals to produce antibodies by deliberately infecting them with certain germs. Blood could then be drawn off and the antibodies in the blood could be concentrated into a serum. This serum could be injected into human beings to give them immunity, without making them go through the disease first.

In 1892 a diphtheria antitoxin (a serum containing antibodies that neutralized the toxin produced by diphtheria germs) was developed by von Behring and Ehrlich. Ehrlich worked out the treatment for prevention of diphtheria, using this antitoxin. His technique has been used all over the world ever since. This achievement won him a professorship at the University of Berlin.

Ehrlich quarreled with von Behring, however, and left him in anger. Ehrlich always quarreled with his coworkers. Although a kindly man, he had his own notions about how to run experiments. Anyone who worked for him or with him had to do exactly what Ehrlich told him to do or leave. Most people endured this treatment, for Ehrlich was usually right.

In 1896 the German government, impressed by the diphtheria antitoxin, opened an institute for serum research and Ehrlich was put in charge. From then on, to the end of his life, he was on his own. The research organizations he ran grew larger and more complicated.

He managed to marry and have children, but he was interested in little but his work and an occasional detective story. When his wife forced him to take a vacation, he counted the days until it was over.

Although he continued to develop serum treatments for a number of diseases, Ehrlich wasn't satisfied with "serum therapy" alone. He wanted to discover chemicals that would help the body fight diseases it couldn't handle itself. He discovered a dye called *Trypan Red*, which helped destroy trypanosomes. Thus began the science of killing disease germs with chemicals (chemotherapy).

Ehrlich kept looking for something better. He decided that the action of Trypan Red was caused by the nitrogen atom combinations it contained. Arsenic atoms resembled nitrogen atoms chemically. What about arsenic chemicals?

Arsenic chemicals were poisonous, but the least poisonous arsenic compound then known was one called "atoxyl." (This word means "not toxic.") Ehrlich began by working out the real form of its molecule, which chemists had not yet worked out correctly.

Then Ehrlich started testing it on animals. Just how large a dose could they take? Would it be large enough to kill germs?

He tried changing atoxyl a little, introducing new atoms, shifting old atoms. He tried one variation, a second, a third. He kept a small army of assistants working out careful animal experiments, but he kept his own watchful eyes on every step that was taken.

Ehrlich wanted a chemical that would kill the germ without any harmful effect on the animals themselves — a chemical magic bullet.

Chemical number $50 - 51 - 52 - 122 - 123 - 389 - 390 -$

Ehrlich simply wouldn't give up. Chemical number 418 — "arsenophenylglycine" — worked. It was a powerful killer of trypanosomes. But Ehrlich wasn't satisfied. He had to work on.

Chemical number $600 - 601 - 602$ — Chemical number 606 ("dihydroxydiamino arsenobenzene hydrochloride") was tested in 1907. But the assistant working with it reported that it had no effect. Ehrlich and his institute worked on.

In 1908, Paul Ehrlich received the Nobel Prize in Medicine for his work on serum therapy. If the award had been postponed for two years, he would have received it for something even more important.

In 1909, a Japanese student, Dr. Hata, came to work for Ehrlich. To learn the techniques, Hata repeated some of the experiments that had already been performed. He happened to try chemical number 606 again. This had been discarded as useless two years before. To his amazement, it turned out to be a powerful germ-killer.

At least it killed a certain type of germ called a "spirochete," which had been discovered to cause a serious disease, syphilis.

Ehrlich was thunderstruck. How had it been missed? In 1910 after numerous tests, Ehrlich announced the discovery to an astonished and enthusiastic world. One of the most tragic diseases had been conquered.

Ehrlich named chemical 606 "Salvarsan" (safe arsenic). For the rest of his life, he worked day and night to see to

it that the medical profession used the chemical correctly.

On August 20, 1915, Paul Ehrlich, 61 and worn out by overwork, died.

Salvarsan was the first major victory of chemotherapy. For a long time, it looked as though it might be the only one. The medical profession, looking for chemicals to fight other diseases, was disappointed.

Then, in 1935, the first of the "sulfa drugs" was discovered. Chemotherapy came to life again. Encouraged by that, British doctors began to investigate a curious substance first reported by Alexander Fleming ten years before. That turned out to be penicillin, a nonpoisonous chemical that killed or stopped the growth of many bacteria. It was found to be even a better killer of spirochetes than was Salvarsan.

In the next decade a host of antibiotics (bacteria-killing chemicals produced by one-celled organisms such as molds) were discovered.

Now chemotherapy is on the verge of wiping out many types of infections. The majority of prescriptions written today make use of chemicals unknown 20 years ago. These are helping to lengthen our life span.

This modern advance in disease-fighting chemicals, and serums containing antibodies, goes back to one man — Paul Ehrlich. In one busy lifetime, he developed both serum therapy and chemotherapy.

Darwin and Wallace

They Explored the Beginnings of Life

20

ONE of the most astonishing books ever written appeared in 1859 — a century ago. Only 1,250 copies were printed, and every copy was snapped up on the very first day of publication. More printings were prepared, and they too were swallowed up.

The book kindled a raging fire of argument. It was denounced. It was defended. Eventually, it won out. It is a scientific book and not easy to read. Some of it is now outmoded in the light of new knowledge. Still, it has never lost its popularity. A paperback edition of the book can be bought for fifty cents.

The title of the book is *On the Origin of Species by Means of Natural Selection, or the Preservation of Favoured Races in the Struggle for Life.* We know it simply as *The Origin of Species.* The author was an English naturalist named Charles Robert Darwin.

Charles Robert Darwin was born in England on February 12, 1809 (the very day on which in an obscure log cabin in the American wilderness, Abraham Lincoln was born). Unlike Lincoln, Darwin was born in comfortable circumstances of a distinguished family. Darwin's father and grandfather were physicians. His grandfather, Dr. Erasmus Darwin, was also a poet and a naturalist.

Darwin's schooling was at first pointed toward medicine. He even went to Edinburgh, Scotland, to begin his medical training. He quickly found he had no desire to study medicine. During this time, however, he met and grew friendly with various scientists. Thus he discovered he wanted to be a naturalist, like his grandfather.

The turning point in his life came in 1831, when he joined the crew of the *Beagle*. This was a ship making a five-year voyage about the world to explore various coast lines and increase man's knowledge of geography. Darwin went along as naturalist, studying the animal and plant life of far places.

The first stop was Tenerife, in the Canary Islands. Brazil was the next stop. There Darwin hunted insects and rheas (large birds which have lost the power of flight). As they traveled southward, Darwin noticed that as the climate changed, plant and animal types also changed. Along the west coast of South America, where the climate is different from that of the east coast, he saw many types that lived only on the west coast. He also dug up the skeletons of fossil animals that were different from the animals then alive.

Darwin noticed a curious thing about "species." (A "species" is a special kind of plant or animal that interbreeds only among itself. Dogs and foxes are separate species, for instance, but collies and terriers are not.) Darwin noted that on the Galapagos Islands (a group of islands off the coast of Ecuador in South America) each island had its own species of a bird resembling the English finch. (These are still called "Darwin's finches" to this day.) He found no fewer than 14 types of finch each slightly different from the other. Some had long beaks, some short beaks, some thin beaks, and some had hooked beaks.

Now why should each little island have its own species? Could it be there was only one species to begin with, but that living on separate islands had split them into several species, each with a beak especially suited for gathering the food (seeds, worms, or insects) that type of finch ate? Could one species change into another?

After leaving the Galapagos Islands, the *Beagle* crossed the Pacific and stopped at ports in Australia and at islands along its coast. Darwin wondered why the kangaroo, the wombat, and the wallaby lived in Australia but were found nowhere else. He reasoned that Australia is really a large island that had once been part of Asia. But the sea rose in some places and cut it off from the mainland.

After it had been separated from the mainland, living things on the island changed. New species appeared. Darwin came to the conclusion that species change.

After Darwin returned home, he spent many years considering these changes in species. Until his time, few people believed it was possible for a species to change, and no one had worked out a good reason to account for the change. Darwin needed a reason.

About this time, he came across a famous book written by a clergyman named T. R. Malthus. Malthus held that population always increased faster than the food supply, so that some people would always be dying of starvation.

Of course! thought Darwin. All animals bring forth

many more young than can possibly live on the food supply available. Some would have to die to make room for the others. Which would die? Obviously, those that weren't as fit as the others for the particular surroundings in which they lived.

To illustrate what this means, suppose one group of dogs were taken to Alaska to live, and another group to Mexico. The dogs in Alaska who happened to have somewhat heavier coats of hair would survive the cold weather better. The dogs in Mexico who had been born with light coats of hair would stand the hot weather better. After a while, only shaggy dogs would exist in Alaska, only sleek ones in Mexico. There also would be other changes because of other differences in the surroundings. After many thousands of years, there might be so many differences that the two groups of dogs would have become too different to interbreed. Instead of one species, there would now be two. This is an example of what Darwin called "natural selection."

Darwin started a book on his theory in 1844 and in 1858 he was still working at it. His friends urged him to hurry or someone else would get there first. Darwin, however, was not to be hurried — and someone else *did* get there first.

The man who got there first was Alfred Russel Wallace, another Englishman, 14 years younger than Darwin.

Wallace's life was quite like that of Darwin. He, too, became early interested in nature. And he, too, joined an expedition to distant lands.

He traveled to tropical South America and also to the East Indies. In the East Indies he noticed that the plants and animals living in the eastern islands of that group (continuing on down into Australia) were completely different from those in the western islands (continuing on up into Asia). The line between the two types of life was sharp, curving between various islands. That line is still called "Wallace's Line" to this day.

In 1855 while in Borneo, Wallace began to think that species must change with time. Then in 1858 he too began to think of Malthus' book, and decided changes took place by natural selection, which he called "the survival of the fittest."

But there was this difference between Darwin and Wallace. After 14 years, Darwin was still working on his book. Wallace was not that type. He got his idea, sat down to write, and was finished in two days.

And to whom did Wallace send the manuscript for consideration and criticism? Why, to the famous naturalist, Charles Darwin, of course.

When Darwin received the manuscript, he was thunderstruck. It was exactly like his own thoughts. Wallace even used similar language. Darwin was a true scientist.

Although he had been working so long on the theory (and had witnesses to prove it), he did not try to keep all the credit. He passed on Wallace's work at once to other important scientists. A paper signed by both men appeared in the *Journal of the Linnaean Society* that year.

The next year, Darwin finally produced his great book, *The Origin of Species*, and his public was ready and waiting for him.

The biggest hole in Darwin's reasoning was his lack of knowledge as to exactly how parents passed on their characteristics to their descendants, and why descendants should vary among themselves. Mendel answered this

question in 1865, only six years after Darwin's book was published, but Mendel's work remained undiscovered until 1900 (see page 107). Darwin died on April 19, 1882, and never learned much about the laws of heredity. Wallace lived on to 1913, and was aware of the work of Mendel and other geneticists.

Darwin is usually thought of as the originator of the "theory of evolution," the theory that life began in simple forms, slowly changed, and grew more complex until the modern species resulted.

He was not the originator, of course. Many thinkers before Darwin, particularly a Frenchman named Jean Baptiste de Lamarck, had presented such theories earlier. (Lamarck's theory came 50 years earlier.) Even Darwin's grandfather had such a theory and wrote a long poem about it.

The great advance of Darwin and Wallace was to work out the theory of natural selection to explain changes in species. More important still, Darwin presented a tremendous amount of evidence and logical reasoning to back up the theory of natural selection.

Once Darwin's book came out, biologists had no choice but to accept his evidence. Until then, changes in species had been merely a speculation. After 1859 they were accepted as a fact. They still are.

The Darwin-Wallace idea revolutionized the outlook of biologists. It made the science of life a single science. Man, himself, took his place in the scheme of life. He, too, like other species, appeared to have developed from simpler forms.

Marie and Pierre Curie

They Paved the Way for the Atomic Age

21

THE young couple, Pierre and Marie Curie, began by obtaining a ton of waste material from the mines in St. Joachimsthal, Bohemia. The mine owners were glad to give it away, but they explained that the Curies would have to pay for shipping it to Paris.

The couple paid. It took almost all the money they had.

The next step was to find a place to work. Marie taught at a girls' school. On the grounds was an unused shed that was practically falling down. Could they use it? The director of the school shrugged. "Go ahead."

The roof leaked, there was practically no heat, no way of using decent chemical equipment. Still the couple pitched in.

The lumps of black rock were samples of an ore called pitchblende. It contained small amounts of uranium. Only two years before, Henri Antoine Becquerel had found that uranium gave off penetrating radiations (see page 124).

But the Curies were after more than uranium. They dissolved batches of the pitchblende in acids, treated it with chemicals, separated some of its elements. Thus they divided the pitchblende into fractions, then kept those fractions that contained the material they were seeking. They were after radiations stronger than those from uranium — much stronger.

They combined the desired fractions from different batches of pitchblende and divided the combined material into new, smaller fractions.

Weeks, months, years — It was backbreaking work, but the fractions became smaller and the radiations they gave off grew stronger.

After four years, in 1902, the ton of pitchblende was reduced to a three-hundredth of an ounce of pure white powder. It was a compound of a new element, one no man had ever seen before. Its radiations were so powerful the glass container which held it could be seen to glow in the dark.

That glow made the four years of work well worthwhile to the Curies. They had put the phenomenon of "radio-activity" on the scientific map, in letters a mile high.

Marie Sklodowska was born in Warsaw on November 7, 1867. Poland at that time was not a good place to live, especially for a young girl with a devouring curiosity to learn about the world. That part of Poland was domi-nated by Tsarist Russia. Education for Poles was not en-couraged. Polish girls were not allowed to go to college.

Marie was not to be stopped, though. When she finished

high school, she borrowed books and tried to teach herself chemistry. Working as a tutor and as a governess, she saved up enough money to send a sister to Paris. In 1891 she was able to go there herself. The French had a history of sympathy for the oppressed Poles that dated back to the time of Napoleon. Many Poles found refuge in Paris. Marie could be sure of friends.

But it was more than friends she needed. It was education. She registered at France's most famous school, the Sorbonne, and began absorbing whatever they could give her. She slept in unheated attics and had so little to eat that she fainted in the classroom. But she finished in first place.

In 1894 a second stroke of good fortune occurred. She met a young man named Pierre Curie and the two fell in love. Pierre had already made a name for himself in physics. He and his brother Jacques had discovered that certain crystals would develop a positive electric charge on one side and a negative one on the other if they were put under pressure. The greater the pressure, the greater the charge. This phenomenon is called "piezoelectricity" (from the Greek *piezein*, "to press," plus electricity). Use is made of it to this day in microphones, radio receivers, and phonographs. Every large radio transmitter is held on frequency by a piezoelectric crystal.

In 1895 Marie and Pierre were married. Marie (now

studying for her doctor's degree) obtained permission to work with her husband, and the two combined work and domestic life. Their first daughter, Irene, was born in 1897.

The world of science was then at the beginning of a revolution. The air was charged with new ideas. Roentgen had discovered X rays. Becquerel had discovered that the radiation from uranium compounds could discharge an electroscope. He was able to show qualitatively that several compounds of uranium do this, but the equipment available to him was too crude to enable him to make minute quantitative measurements. The electrometer devised by Pierre Curie and his brother Jacques, using piezoelectricity, could measure extremely small amounts of current. Marie Curie decided to use this device to study uranium radiation quantitatively.

This was the principle involved: The rays from uranium knocked electrons from atoms in air. Left behind were "ions" which could carry an electric current. Thus the strength of the uranium rays could be determined by measuring the amount of electric current they enabled air to carry. The current could be measured by balancing it against one of Pierre's crystals under different pressures. At a certain pressure, the crystal would develop a high enough charge to stop the current.

Marie Curie found that the amount of radiation is always

proportional to the number of uranium atoms, regardless of how they are chemically combined with other elements. She discovered that another heavy metal, thorium, also gave off similar rays.

She had scarcely passed her thirtieth birthday. It was only six years since she had arrived in Paris, but she was already making a name for herself. Pierre saw clearly that his brilliant young wife was on the track of something big. He abandoned his own research and joined her.

Uranium metal was obtained mostly from the mineral pitchblende. When the Curies wanted more uranium, they would get it from a piece of ore. Naturally, they would check the ore to see whether that particular piece had enough uranium to make it worth their while. To do

this they had to measure the radioactivity of the ore.

One day in 1898 they stumbled on a piece of pitchblende that was so radioactive it would have had to contain more uranium atoms than could possibly be in it.

The Curies, astonished, came to the only possible conclusion. There were elements in the pitchblende that were even more radioactive than uranium. No such elements were known, so new and undiscovered elements must be involved. But no strange elements had ever been noted in pitchblende. Well, then, they must be present in very small quantities. But for small quantities to show that much radiation, the new elements must be very, very radioactive indeed. It worked out as inevitably as A, B, C.

The Curies began fractionating the pitchblende, follow-

ing the radioactivity. They removed the uranium and, sure enough, most of the radioactivity remained behind. By July of that year they had isolated a trace of black powder 400 times more radioactive than uranium. This contained a new element which behaved like tellurium (an element that was not radioactive). They decided to call the new element "polonium" after Marie's native land.

But that accounted for only part of the radioactivity. More fractionation followed, and more painstaking work. By December of that same year they had a preparation which was even more radioactive than polonium. This contained still another element, which had properties like those of the well known, nonradioactive element barium. The Curies called their new element "radium."

But their best preparations still contained only a trace of the new element. What they needed was enough of the element to be seen and weighed and tested. There was so little of it in pitchblende, however, that the Curies would have to start with a great deal of ore. So they got their ton of mine wastes and labored four more years.

In 1903, Marie Sklodowska Curie presented her work on radioactivity as her doctor's thesis and received her Ph.D. It was probably the greatest doctor's thesis in history. It earned her not one, but *two* Nobel Prizes. In 1903 she and Pierre, along with Henri Becquerel, were awarded the Physics Prize for their studies of uranium radiations. In 1911, Marie Curie received the Chemistry Prize for the discovery of polonium and radium.

The second prize, Marie received alone, for in 1906 Pierre Curie had died tragically in a traffic accident.

Marie worked on. She took over the professorship at the Sorbonne Pierre had held, and became the first woman professor in the Sorbonne's history. She worked ceaselessly, studying the properties and dangers of her wonderful elements. She deliberately exposed herself to radiations to study the burns caused on her skin.

In July 1934, revered by the whole world as one of the greatest women of history, Marie Curie died of leukemia, a disease that was probably brought on by her continuous exposure to radioactive radiations.

Had she lived a year longer, she would have seen a third Nobel Prize awarded to Curies — this time to her daughter Irene and her son-in-law Frederic. They had created brand-new radioactive atoms and were the discoverers of "artificial radioactivity."

In 1946 element number 96 was discovered at the University of California. It was named "curium" as an eternal honor to the Curies.

Roentgen and Becquerel, with their discoveries of mysterious radiations, began a new scientific revolution, equal to that begun by Copernicus in 1500.

That first revolution had been dramatized by Galileo

and his telescope. This second revolution also needed a dramatist, someone who could lift the radiations out of the scientific journals and onto the front page of newspapers. The Curies and their radium did that.

Their work was important scientifically (and medically, too, for small pinches of radium and similar elements were used to fight cancer). But more than that, their work was supremely dramatic. Partly it was because a woman was so intimately involved; partly it was because of the great difficulties that had to be overcome; partly it was because of the results.

The Curies did not single-handedly hurl mankind into the age of the atom. Indeed, the work of Roentgen, Becquerel, Einstein and other scientists was of even greater importance. But the heroic immigrant girl from Poland and her husband helped to give the world a sense of expectation of still greater things to come.

Albert Einstein

He Charted a New World

22

ON MARCH 29, 1919, an eclipse of the sun took place that was destined to be one of the most important in the history of mankind. For years astronomers of London's Royal Astronomical Society had been waiting eagerly for this eclipse. It would enable them to check a revolutionary new theory in physics proposed four years earlier by a German-born scientist named Albert Einstein.

On the day of the eclipse, one group of astronomers was stationed in northern Brazil, another on an island off West Africa. Delicate cameras were set up and waiting. When the eclipse occurred, photographs would be taken — not of the eclipsed sun, but of the stars that suddenly appeared in the darkened sky around the sun.

Einstein had said the stars would be found to have shifted their apparent position. The rays of starlight passing near the sun would be bent by the sun's mass. This sounded impossible. How could light, which was immaterial, be affected by gravity? If Einstein were correct, the picture of the universe built up by the great Isaac Newton more than two hundred years earlier would have to be corrected in some of its details.

The eclipse came. The pictures were taken and developed. The distances of the star images from the sun and from each other were painstakingly measured. These measurements were compared with measurements on a star map of that region of the sky taken at night, with the sun nowhere near.

There could be no doubt. The astronomers announced the results: The light rays were bent out of their straight path by the attraction of the sun. Einstein was right. One of the predictions of his theory was verified.

Albert Einstein was born in Germany on March 14, 1879. As a child he had difficulty in learning to speak. His parents suspected he might be mentally retarded. He was not a brilliant student in secondary school. He chafed under the monotonous drill methods of teaching used in German schools at that time. Nor was he able to finish his studies. In 1894 his father's business failed and the family moved to Milan, Italy. Young Einstein, who had grown interested in science, went to Zurich, Switzerland, to enter a famous technical school. There his unusual ability in mathematics and physics began to show itself.

However, when Einstein was graduated in 1900 he was unable to get a teaching appointment at a university. He was lucky to get a clerical job in the patent office at Bern, Switzerland. It was not what he wanted, but it would give him leisure for studying and thinking.

There was much to think about. The old structure of physics, built up over centuries, was being restudied in the light of new knowledge.

For instance, it was believed that light traveled through the vacuum of space. Since light consisted of waves, something had to exist in space to form those waves. Physicists decided that space was full of something called "ether." It was the vibration of this "ether" that formed light waves.

It was assumed that the true motion of Earth could be measured against this ether. This could be done by noting how quickly light traveled along the line of Earth's motion as compared with its velocity across Earth's motion. (Just as you can tell the speed of a river's current by measuring how quickly you can row downstream when the current is helping you, as compared with your speed when rowing cross-stream, when the current is not helping you.)

In 1887 this experiment was carried out very delicately by Albert A. Michelson and E. W. Morley, two American scientists. To their amazement, they could find no difference in light's velocity. Was something wrong?

The discovery and study of radioactivity by Becquerel and the Curies created another explosion. Elements such as uranium, thorium, and radium were giving off vast quantities of energy. Where did this energy come from?

The whole structure of physics was based on the fact that neither matter nor energy could be created or destroyed. Must the whole structure of physics be torn down?

In 1905 Albert Einstein, then 26, published his thoughts on these questions. He said, suppose light traveled at *constant* velocity regardless of the motion of its place of origin, as the Michelson-Morley experiment seemed to show. In that case, what would the consequences be?

He demonstrated those consequences in clear, straightforward mathematics. There could be no such thing as absolute motion, said Einstein, or absolute lack of motion. Earth moved in one fashion if you compared its position in space with that of the sun. It moved in another fashion if you compared its position with that of Mars; and so on.

Furthermore, in measuring length, mass, or even time the relative motion between the object measured and the measuring observer affected the results of the comparison.

Matter and energy, Einstein said, were different aspects of the same thing. Matter could be converted into energy, and energy into matter. In radioactivity a tiny bit of matter was converted to energy. So little matter was converted that its loss could not be measured by ordinary weighing. The energy produced out of this bit of matter was large enough to be detected, however.

It all seemed to go against "common sense," but it all hung together. And it explained things that scientists could not explain any other way.

In 1909 the fame that resulted from his theories got

Einstein a job at the University of Prague, and in 1913 he was appointed director of a new research institution opened in Berlin, the Kaiser Wilhelm Physics Institute.

In 1915, during World War I, Einstein published a paper that extended his theories. He put forth new views on the nature of gravitation. Newton's theories, he said, were not accurate enough. The inaccuracy showed up most glaringly in the close neighborhood of large masses such as the sun.

Einstein's theories seemed to explain the slow rotation of the entire orbit of the planet Mercury (closest planet to the sun), which Newton's theories could not explain. Einstein's theories also predicted that light rays passing near the sun would be bent out of a straight line. When this was verified at the eclipse of 1919, Einstein was instantly accepted as the greatest scientific thinker since Newton.

In 1921 Einstein received the Nobel Prize in Physics — not for relativity, but for presenting a logical explanation of the "photoelectric effect." This solved the riddle of how the application of light was able to make electrons come out of certain materials. He was also honored for his theories dealing with "Brownian movement" — the movement of tiny particles suspended in liquid or air. This phenomenon had puzzled physicists for nearly 80 years.

Then Germany fell upon evil days. Adolf Hitler and his Nazis began to grow stronger. The Nazis preached anti-Semitism in a new and brutal form — and Albert Einstein was Jewish. In January 1933, when the Nazis came to power, Einstein happened to be in California. Prudently, he did not return to Germany. He went to Belgium instead. The Nazis confiscated Einstein's possessions, publicly burned his writings, and expelled him from all German scientific societies.

Einstein emigrated to the United States. America was glad to have him (he became an American citizen in 1940 by special Act of Congress). He was invited to join the Institute for Advanced Studies at Princeton, N. J.

In 1934 an Italian physicist, Enrico Fermi, began bombarding elements with newly discovered sub-atomic particles called "neutrons." He noted peculiar results when uranium was bombarded, but he had no satisfactory explanation. (The importance of this work was recognized when Fermi was awarded the 1938 Nobel Prize in Physics.) A few years later, in Berlin, the chemist Otto Hahn discovered that bombarding uranium with neutrons produced atoms of about half the weight of uranium.

A possible explanation of Hahn's work was advanced in 1938 by Lise Meitner and O. R. Frisch, two German refugee physicists doing research in Copenhagen, Denmark. When uranium atoms were struck by neutrons, they said, some of the atoms broke in two. This was "uranium fission." Uranium fission released far more energy than did ordinary radioactivity. It also released neutrons that could trigger off additional explosions of uranium atoms. The result could be the most terrifying explosion ever seen. Hahn's experiment showed that mass and energy were related, as Einstein said they were.

In January 1939, the Danish physicist Niels Bohr came to the U. S. to spend several months at Princeton. There he planned to discuss various problems with Einstein. At Princeton, Bohr announced Hahn's observations and what Frisch and Meitner had said. Their theory quickly came to the attention of Fermi, who had fled from Italy (then allied with Hitler's Germany) and was working at Columbia University.

Fermi discussed the subject with physicists John R. Dunning and George Pegram of Columbia. It was arranged for Dunning to set up an experiment as quickly as possible to check Hahn's results and the theory of Frisch and Meitner. Dunning worked around the clock for several days. He performed the first experiment in America that demonstrated it was possible to split the atom.

In the summer of 1939, these new developments were discussed with Albert Einstein. He sent a letter to President Franklin D. Roosevelt, pointing out that atomic bombs were possible and that enemy nations must not be allowed to devise them first.

Roosevelt agreed with Einstein. Funds for research were appropriated. The Atomic Age began to dawn.

On April 18, 1955, Albert Einstein died. To his dying day, he urged the world to come to some agreement that would make nuclear wars forever impossible.

Einstein was the Newton of the scientific revolution that had begun with Roentgen and Becquerel. His theories enabled scientists to predict developments and search them out. Thus, as soon as uranium fission was discovered, Einstein's theories pointed to the possibility of an atomic bomb and atomic power.

All that happens in the future with respect to atomic power — whether for good or for evil — dates back to the equations a young patent clerk first introduced to express the relationship between matter and energy.

George Washington Carver

World in a Peanut

23

THE young botanist had a difficult decision to make in that year of 1896. After great hardships, he had become a respected scientist at Iowa State College. He earned a decent living. He could experiment with growing plants to his heart's content.

Now a small poverty-stricken college in Alabama wanted him. He would have to leave his good life in Iowa, and return to a land where he would have a lowly status.

Yet the botanist could not refuse. The college that wanted him was Tuskegee Institute. It was the only place in all the South where Negroes could get a higher education — and the young botanist was a Negro. His name was George Washington Carver.

So Carver turned his back on the success his efforts had brought him and returned to the South. There still greater success awaited him.

George Washington Carver was born about 1864. There is no record of the exact date of his birth in Diamond Grove, Missouri, but it was some time near the end of the

Civil War. He was a slave until the passage of the Thirteenth Amendment in 1865.

When he was only a few months old, night raiders stole him and his mother. The mother was sold and shipped away before her master, Moses Carver, could save her. He was able to ransom the infant by trading a horse for him.

The Carvers adopted the infant after he was freed. As the boy grew up, he showed signs of considerable intelligence, but the Carvers were unable to help him get an education at home. The town had no school for Negro children. So the Carvers sent him to the county seat, Neosho. There he attended a one-room school with about 70 other Negro children and one teacher. He worked to support himself while he studied, but his marks were excellent. He continued to study and work at odd jobs until he completed high school. Then he determined to go on to college.

It was not easy at that time to find a college that would admit a Negro. Eventually he was accepted by Simpson College, at Indianola, Iowa. George Washington Carver was then 25, the first Negro to be accepted by Simpson College. He did so well that on graduation he had no trouble getting into Iowa State Agricultural College for further studies. When he was granted a master of science degree there in 1892, he was appointed to the staff.

Then came the call to Tuskegee, founded by Booker T. Washington, the great Negro educator. Carver became director of Tuskegee's Department of Agricultural Research.

Starting with 19 acres of the "worst land in Alabama," Carver showed his students how to rebuild the soil with muck from nearby swamps and compost heaps they could make themselves.

The Southern farmer had one chief problem: the soil was worn out. For generations, only cotton and tobacco had been grown in most of the South. The plants had taken minerals out of the soil — more than had been put back.

George Washington Carver knew that soil which might be worn out for one crop could still grow another crop well. He knew, too, that this "rotation of crops" could restore needed nitrogen to soil. His experiments at Tuskegee backed this up, and he carried on a ceaseless campaign of education to get Southern farmers to use variety in planting. He wanted them to plant peanuts and sweet potatoes instead of cotton — at least part of the time.

Almost single-handedly he won his way. The result? The Southern farmer found his land being restored, his crops and income improving. Indeed, so large were the

crops of peanuts and sweet potatoes that not all of them could be sold for food. Now what?

Carver went to work in his laboratory. He took the peanut apart — separating its oils, starches, amino acids. Then he recombined these in new ways.

Carver developed about 300 synthetic products from peanuts, including cheese, dyes, and soap. He made the sweet potato yield 118 synthetic products, including molasses, paste, and rubber. He showed that a farm crop wasn't merely food. It was raw material which the magic of chemistry could convert into a horn of plenty.

Now the Southern farmer could grow all the peanuts and sweet potatoes he wished. He could also grow soybeans, for Carver introduced that valuable plant from China. The soybean grows well in poor soil and helps to replace nitrogen at the same time.

George Washington Carver's research in chemistry accomplished wonders for agriculture. He was honored by being made a fellow of the Royal Society of Arts of London. In 1923 he won the Spingarn Medal, awarded to outstanding members of his race. In 1939 he won the Roosevelt Medal. The citation read: "To a scientist humbly seeking the guidance of God and a liberator to men of the white race as well as the black."

Many honorary degrees were awarded to Carver. But he was a simple man, content to pass on his learning to new generations at Tuskegee, where he taught until he passed away in 1943.

Irving Langmuir

He Made Rain

24

Even during droughts, water vapor and clouds are in the air. Why, then, doesn't rain fall?

Apparently, dust particles were also necessary. Rain drops formed around dust particles.

At the General Electric Company, in Schenectady, N. Y., the associate director of research, Irving Langmuir, had a home-made cloud in the laboratory — a box filled with water vapor. He would cool it and add various kinds of dust.

One hot day, a little more than a decade ago, there was trouble keeping the box cool enough. Langmuir decided to use dry ice (frozen carbon dioxide). He added pieces of it to the box and at once the vapor it contained turned into a thousand swirling little particles of ice. A miniature snow storm had formed out of the miniature cloud. Dust wasn't absolutely necessary after all — just a low enough temperature, 40 degrees below zero or less.

In 1946, then, an airplane flew over a cloudbank. It carried powdered dry ice which was dropped into the clouds. Half an hour later it was raining — the first truly man-made rain.

Irving Langmuir was born in Brooklyn, New York, on January 31, 1881. His parents traveled constantly, and his early education was spread across two continents. At Columbia University he earned his degree in metallurgical engineering in 1903. Then it was back to Germany, this time for his Ph.D. in physical chemistry, which he received in 1906.

After a short time teaching, Langmuir joined the staff of General Electric in 1909. He stayed there for almost 50 years. His first job was to devise methods for extending the life span of light bulbs, then very short.

At that time the tungsten filaments in light bulbs were enclosed in vacuum. (If air were present, the tungsten would burn up as soon as it was heated.) Langmuir's studies showed that in the vacuum (which could not be made perfect), tungsten atoms slowly evaporated from the wire at the white hot temperature of the glowing bulb. The wire grew thinner and eventually broke. If the bulb were filled with gas — some gas with which tungsten would not react (nitrogen or argon, for instance) — the filament would last longer. Thus the gas-filled bulb was invented.

Langmuir then studied the effect of hot metal surfaces on all sorts of gases. It led him in many directions that had nothing to do with gas bulbs, but General Electric recognized his genius and gave him complete freedom.

For example, Langmuir devised a hydrogen blowtorch that could produce temperatures almost as hot as the surface of the sun. This was the principle: A molecule of ordinary hydrogen is made up of two atoms. If a stream of hydrogen is heated to a high temperature by being blown past hot tungsten wires, some of the two-atom hydrogen molecules are broken up into free hydrogen atoms. These atoms are very active. Therefore, as the jet of gas leaves the tungsten filament, the free hydrogen atoms recombine to form ordinary two-atom hydrogen again. At the same time, they give up as heat the energy they received from the hot tungsten. The temperature inside the hydrogen gas is about 6,000 degrees.

Langmuir grew interested in how matter spread out on various types of surfaces — on liquid surfaces, for instance. A drop of mineral oil (which is insoluble in water) will, when placed on water, hold together in the shape of a lens. However, stearic acid (also insoluble in water) con-

tains certain groupings of atoms which are attracted to water. A drop of stearic acid, when added to water, spreads out into a thin film, as each molecule tries to dip its water-loving group into the water. In fact, the film may be one molecule thick. Langmuir was the first to show this and to study such films.

For his work in surface chemistry, Langmuir received the Nobel Prize for Chemistry in 1932. (Rain-making — which he worked on with Dr. Vincent J. Schaefer — was still in the future.)

The useful results of Langmuir's work were many. His studies of films, for instance, have given us ways to cut down glare from glass surfaces — an important safety measure. However, it is rain-making that was probably the most important breakthrough. Langmuir's system was later improved by Dr. Bernard Vonnegut of General Electric. He found that a cloud of fine particles of a chemical called silver iodide worked even better than did dry ice. Besides, the silver iodide could be generated on the ground and blown skyward.

Langmuir died in 1957, living to see rain-making become a big business.

Some day we may be able to nip hurricanes in the bud by causing a hurricane-breeding area to drop its rain prematurely — thanks to the small cloud in the General Electric laboratories.

Rutherford and Lawrence

They Tore Apart the Atom

25

ERNEST RUTHERFORD was after big game. At least it was "big game" in the world of science, though his quarry was the tiny atom, only a few billionths of an inch in diameter. The question was: What was inside that atom?

For a century, scientists had believed that the atom was the smallest particle which could exist, and that it was shaped like a billiard ball. Then, in the 1890's, still smaller particles had been discovered. It was found that radio-active atoms break down, spraying smaller "sub-atomic" particles in all directions.

To find out what was inside the tiny atom, therefore, Rutherford aimed still tinier bullets at it. He used the sub-atomic particles sprayed out by radioactive atoms.

These particles were so small and moved so quickly that they passed through thin slices of ordinary matter as though nothing were there. A narrow beam of particles would strike a photographic plate and leave a darkened spot, even though a thin sheet of metal blocked their path. In 1906 Rutherford noticed that the metal had a strange effect. The darkened spot was fuzzy, as though some particles had been pushed to one side in passing through the metal.

In 1908 Rutherford and his assistant, Hans Geiger, decided to investigate this phenomenon. They would fire particles at gold leaf beaten to a thinness of only one fifty-thousandth of an inch. Even at this thinness, the wall of the gold leaf was 2,000 atoms thick. If atoms filled all the space, reasoned Rutherford, the particles would have no chance of getting through.

But the particles did get through. Practically every one came through in a straight line. A few came through at an angle, like a billiard ball struck off its center. One particle in 20,000 actually bounced back.

How could that be? Rutherford said afterward that it was as though a cannon ball had been fired at a piece of tissue paper and had bounced back into the cannon.

Rutherford finally decided upon an explanation. Most of the atom was empty space, through which sub-particles could pass easily. At the center of each atom, though, was a tiny nucleus which contained practically all the mass of the atom. This nucleus was surrounded by particles which revolved about it in orbits, like planets.

Rutherford was thus the first to discover what the inside of the atom was like. These experiments were conducted in 1908. In that year he received the Nobel Prize

in Chemistry — for work he had done earlier. Thus, his greatest work came *after* he got the prize.

Ernest Rutherford was truly a scientist of the British Empire. He worked in Canada and in England, but he was born in New Zealand on August 30, 1871. In college, where his talent for physics first showed itself, he won a scholarship to Cambridge University. There he studied under a great British scientist, J. J. Thomson.

Rutherford began his work in the field of electricity and magnetism, but in 1895 (the year Rutherford had come to England) Wilhelm Roentgen rocked the scientific world by his discovery of X rays. Thomson at once decided to strike out in this new direction, and Rutherford gladly went along.

Rutherford showed himself to be so able, that when there was a vacancy on the faculty at McGill University in Montreal, Thomson recommended him. In 1898 off went Rutherford to Canada.

In 1899 Rutherford found there were at least two kinds of radiations given off by radioactive substances. He named them "alpha rays" and "beta rays," after the first two letters of the Greek alphabet. Both rays were streams of sub-atomic particles, it later turned out. The alpha rays were composed of particularly massive particles. Rutherford eventually used them as bullets to probe the atom. In 1903 he and a student named Frederick Soddy worked out the mathematics describing the rate at which a radioactive substance broke down.

By 1908 Rutherford had discovered how to detect individual sub-atomic particles. He allowed them to strike a film of zinc sulfide so that a tiny flash was produced. The zinc sulfide "scintillated." With this "scintillation screen," Rutherford could follow and count individual particles.

By using the bullets he had discovered and the counter he had developed, Rutherford was able to probe the inside of the atom. Ten years later, he did something even more startling. He used his bullets not on metals but on gases.

When Rutherford sent alpha rays hurtling through hydrogen gas, they struck some of the nuclei of the hydrogen atoms. These atoms were composed of simple particles called "protons." When these protons were knocked into a zinc sulfide screen, they gave rise to a particular type of bright scintillation. When Rutherford bombarded oxygen, carbon dioxide, or water vapor, nothing startling happened. When he bombarded nitrogen, the proton scintillations suddenly appeared.

Where did the protons come from? There was only one answer possible. When alpha rays struck the nucleus of the nitrogen atom, they knocked protons out of it. The nitrogen was changed into a rare isotope of oxygen. The proton was observed as a product of the reaction.

Rutherford was thus the first man to change one element (nitrogen) into another (oxygen). He had brought about, in 1919, the first man-made nuclear reaction.

Through the years, more and more investigations of atomic structure were made. Needed for this purpose were faster sub-atomic bullets and more of them. Alpha rays were all right, but they lacked high energy, and the radioactive substances that gave off alpha rays were difficult to obtain.

Scientists tried to use protons instead, which could be obtained easily from hydrogen. Protons were not as heavy as the particles in alpha rays, but they could be speeded up to great energies by an accelerating electric field, in which they were held on course by magnets. The man who showed how best to do this was another Ernest — Ernest Orlando Lawrence, born in Canton, South Dakota, on August 8, 1901.

In 1930, as a young man at the University of California, Lawrence got to thinking about speeding up protons. The difficulty was that they finally sped right out of range of the magnets which held them on course. How could they be kept inside the instrument until they had gained enough speed to be useful? Why not, thought Lawrence, make the protons go around in circles?

At once, he built a home-made gadget in which he arranged electromagnets in an ingenious fashion. The protons were forced to travel in circles, speeding up all the time. Eventually they shot out of the instrument with amazing force. Lawrence called the instrument a "cyclotron," because the particles moved in circles.

By 1931, a larger cyclotron than the original one was built for $1,000. It produced protons with energies of over a million electron volts. Before long, by using still larger cyclotrons, particles were given energies of 100,000,-000 electron volts. Today improved instruments based on the cyclotron principle can produce particles with energies in the billions of electron volts.

Rutherford's original "bullets" had been vastly improved. Atoms could be smashed, and the debris studied in a manner that would have been undreamed of only a few years earlier.

Rutherford passed away in 1937. He lived to see the cyclotron carry on his work. Lawrence lived to see the cyclotron increase atomic knowledge to the point where atomic power became a reality. In fact, in the early 1940's, Lawrence was involved in the research that resulted in development of the first nuclear reactors. He conducted a program for separating out quantities of the rare isotope, uranium-235, and also for producing the man-made element plutonium. The atoms of both could be split in a continuing reaction to yield useful power, or the devastating explosion of an atomic bomb.

Lawrence died in 1958.

As long as radioactivity was only an unusual property of certain rare elements, it was important in theoretical science, but its influence on man's activities was slight.

What Ernest Rutherford did was to turn radioactivity from a phenomenon into a tool. He used sub-atomic particles as bullets with which to split open the atom, enabling him to discover the atomic nucleus.

Ernest Lawrence invented a better tool by which this could be done. As a result of the work of both, the inside of the atom yielded up its secrets at an unbelievably rapid rate. Twenty-three years after the first man-made nuclear reaction, mankind has learned to start one going and keep it controlled as a kind of nuclear "furnace." In the same way, many thousands of years ago, man had learned to start ordinary fires to serve his needs.

Nuclear conflagrations, in the form of atomic bombs, can be a great danger to humanity, but so can ordinary conflagrations. Man has gained immeasurable benefits from ordinary fire, despite its dangers. Will he be as wise with the nuclear fires he now controls?

Robert Hutchings Goddard

He Launched the Space Age

26

THE gasoline mixed with the liquid oxygen and caught fire. Up rose the rocket, blasting through the atmosphere. In a short while the fuel was spent, but the rocket continued soaring to a peak, and then fell.

Where did this take place? Cape Canaveral in the 1950's?

Not at all. It was on a snow-covered farm in Auburn, Massachusetts. The date was March 16, 1926. The first liquid-fueled rocket ever to be shot into the heavens was being tested by a scientist named Robert Hutchings Goddard.

The rocket traveled only 200 feet. It reached a speed of only 60 miles an hour, but the experiment was as important as the Kitty Hawk flight of the Wright brothers. However, no one cared. Goddard, who went on to establish American rocketry single-handed, remained unknown to the public to the day of his death.

Robert Goddard was born in Worcester, Massachusetts, in 1882. He received his Ph.D. at Clark University in 1911. He taught at Princeton, but returned to Clark in

1914. There he began his experiments in rocketry.

In 1919 Goddard prepared a small 69-page book on the theory of rockets. It was called *A Method of Reaching Extreme Altitudes*. Meanwhile, during the previous decade, a Russian named Ziolkovsky had been writing similar articles. (Oddly, Russia and America were competing in rocketry even then, though neither nation knew it.)

The American was the first to put theory into actual practice. In 1923 Goddard tested his first rocket engine, using liquid fuels (gasoline and liquid oxygen). In 1926 he sent up his first rocket. His wife took a picture of him standing next to that rocket. It was about four feet high, six inches in diameter, and held in a frame like a child's jungle gym. This was the grand-daddy of the monsters of Cape Canaveral.

Goddard managed to get a few thousand dollars from the Smithsonian Institution and continued his work. In July 1929 he sent up a larger rocket near Worcester, Massachusetts. It went faster and higher than the first.

More important, it carried a barometer and a thermometer and a small camera to photograph them. It was the first instrument-carrying rocket.

Then Goddard ran into trouble. He already had a small reputation as a "crackpot" who thought he could reach the moon. (This was painful to him because he detested publicity and was mainly interested in studying the upper atmosphere.) His second rocket resulted in calls to the police. Officials ordered him to conduct no more rocket experiments in Massachusetts.

Fortunately, a philanthropist named Daniel Guggenheim gave Goddard some money, enough to enable him to set up an experimental station in a lonely spot in New Mexico. Here he built larger rockets, and developed many of the ideas now used in all rockets. He designed combustion chambers of the proper shape, and burned gasoline with oxygen so that the rapid combustion could be used to cool the chamber walls. He saw at once that the root of the problem was achievement of very high speeds of combustion with respect to the body of the rocket.

From 1930 to 1935 he sent up rockets which attained speeds of up to 550 miles an hour and reached heights of a mile and a half. He developed systems for steering a rocket in flight and gyroscopes to keep a rocket headed in the proper direction. He patented the idea of multi-stage rockets.

But our Government never really became interested in his work. Only during World War II did it finance him, and then it was only to enable him to design small rockets to help Navy planes take off from carriers.

In Germany, meanwhile, a group of men were developing large rockets based on Goddard's principles. They worked out the V-2 rocket, which might have won the war for the Nazis if it had been perfected earlier.

When German rocket experts were brought to America after the war and questioned about the science of rocketry, they stared in amazement. Why didn't the Americans ask Goddard, they wanted to know.

It was too late. Goddard had died on August 10, 1945, just at the time the Atomic Age was dawning.

We are living at the beginning of the Goddard breakthrough. There is no way of telling exactly what benefits will come to mankind from the conquest of space. However, that conquest will increase our knowledge. And this we know: every increase in man's knowledge helps mankind, sometimes in unexpected ways. (Sometimes the misuse of knowledge has hurt mankind; but that is the fault of men, not of knowledge.)

Whatever the future of the rocket, it all began with Goddard's first little rocket, which rose 200 feet over the snow-covered farm in Auburn.

Species, 147
Specific gravity, 7
Spirochete, 143
Spontaneous generation, 102
Steam engine, 54
Steel, 86
Stock-ticker, 132
Sturgeon, William, 78
Sub-atomic particles, 125, 181
Sulfa drugs, 144
Sunspots, 35
Synthetics, 118, 175
Syphilis, 143
Syracuse, 1

Tartaric acid, 99
Tatum, E. L., 110
Telegraph, 76, 130
Telescopes, 34, 48
Third Law of Motion, 50
Thomson, J. J., 125, 184
Thorium, 158
Traité élémentaire de chimie, 65
Transformer, 73
Trypan Red, 141
Trypanosomes, 137
Tschermak, Erich, 107
Tuberculosis, 138
Tungsten filaments, 178
Turks, 15, 92
Tuskegee Institute, 172
Type, movable, 10
Tyrian Purple, 118

Uranium, 154
  neutron bombardment of, 169
  radiations of, 124, 157
Uranium fission, 170
Uranium-235, 187

Vaccination, 96
Vaccine, Salk, 97
Veins, 27
Venus, 19
Vesalius, Andreas, 27
Voltage, 72
Voltaire, 53
Vonnegut, Bernard, 180
V-2 rocket, 193

Waldeyer, Wilhelm von, 138
Wallace, Alfred Russel, 149
Wallace's Line, 150
Washington, Booker T., 174
Washington, George, 92
Watt, James, 54
Weather Bureau, U.S., 82, 83
Wine, souring of, 100
Wrought iron, 86

X-rays, 123
  medical uses of, 126

Yeast, 100

Zinc sulfide, 185